P9-CMF-708

GOSPEL HYMNS

AND

SACRED SONGS.

BY

P. P. BLISS and IRA D. SANKEY,

AS USED BY THEM IN

GOSPEL MEETINGS.

PUBLISHED BY

BIGLOW & MAIN,	JOHN CHURCH & Co.
76 East Ninth Street, New York,	66 West Fourth Street, Cincinnati,
91 Washington Street, Chicago.	Root & Son's Music Co., Chicago.

May be ordered of Booksellers and Music Dealers.

PREFACE.

THIS Collection of GOSPEL HYMNS AND SACRED SONGS, has been compiled with great care, and is believed to contain the most useful and popular pieces to be found in the whole library of Christian Song.

A large number of the hymns were used in the late Special Services in Great Britain, and it is hoped that a like blessing will accompany the use of them in this land, together with the new hymns found in this collection.

P. P. Bliss

Ira D. Sankey

GOSPEL HYMNS

AND

SACRED SONGS.

No. 1. Old Hundred. L. M.

"Come before His presence with singing."—PSA. 100 : 2.

REV. WM. KETHE, 1561. G. FRANC, 1545.

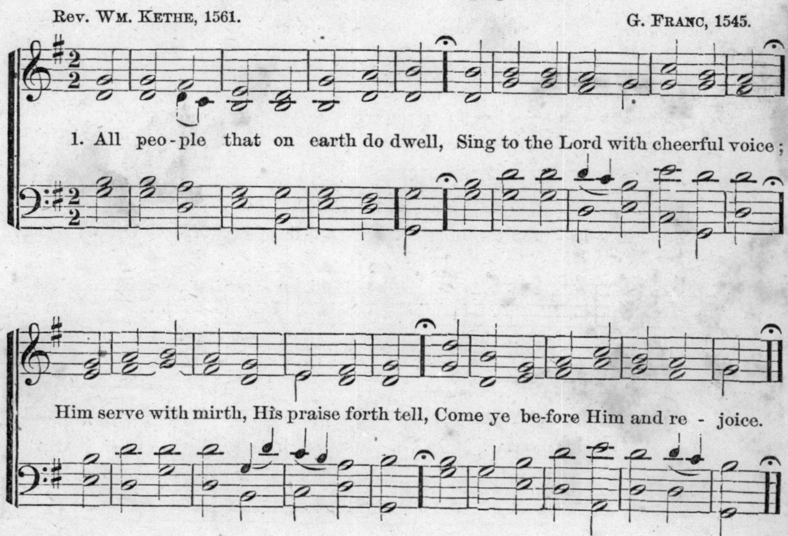
1. All peo-ple that on earth do dwell, Sing to the Lord with cheerful voice;
Him serve with mirth, His praise forth tell, Come ye be-fore Him and re - joice.

2 Know that the Lord is God indeed;
Without our aid He did us make:
We are His flock, He doth us feed,
And for His sheep He doth us take.

3 O enter then His gates with praise,
Approach with joy His courts unto:
Praise, laud, and bless His name always,
For it is seemly so to do.

4 For why? the Lord our God is good,
His mercy is for ever sure;
His truth at all times firmly stood,
And shall from age to age endure.

DOXOLOGY. L. M.

Praise God, from whom all blessings flow;
Praise Him, all creatures here below;
Praise Him above, ye heavenly host;
Praise Father, Son, and Holy Ghost.

BP. THOS. KEN. 1697.

No. 2. Hallelujah, 'tis Done!

"For God so loved the world, that He gave His only begotten Son, that whosoever believeth in Him, should not perish, but have everlasting life."—JOHN 3 : 16.

P. P. BLISS. P. P. BLISS, by per.

1. 'Tis the prom - ise of God, full sal - va - tion to give
2. Tho' the path - way be lone - ly, and dan - ger - ous too,
Un - to him who on Je - sus, his Son, will be - lieve.
Sure - ly Je - sus is a - ble to car - ry me through.
Hal - le - lu - jah, 'tis done! I be - lieve on the Son; I am
saved by the blood of the cru - ci - fied One; cru - ci - fied One.
1st.
2nd.

3 Many loved ones have I in yon heavenly throng,
They are safe now in glory, and this is their song:
Hallelujah, 'tis done! etc.

4 Little children I see standing close by their King,
And He smiles as their song of salvation they sing
Hallelujah, 'tis done! etc.

5 There are prophets and kings in that throng I behold,
And they sing as they march through the streets of pure gold:
Hallelujah, 'tis done! etc.

6 There's a part in that chorus for you and for me,
And the theme of our praises forever will be:
Hallelujah, 'tis done! etc.

No. 3. I Need Thee Every Hour.

"Without Me ye can do nothing." JOHN 15: 5.

Mrs. ANNIE S. HAWKS. Rev. ROBERT LOWRY, by per.

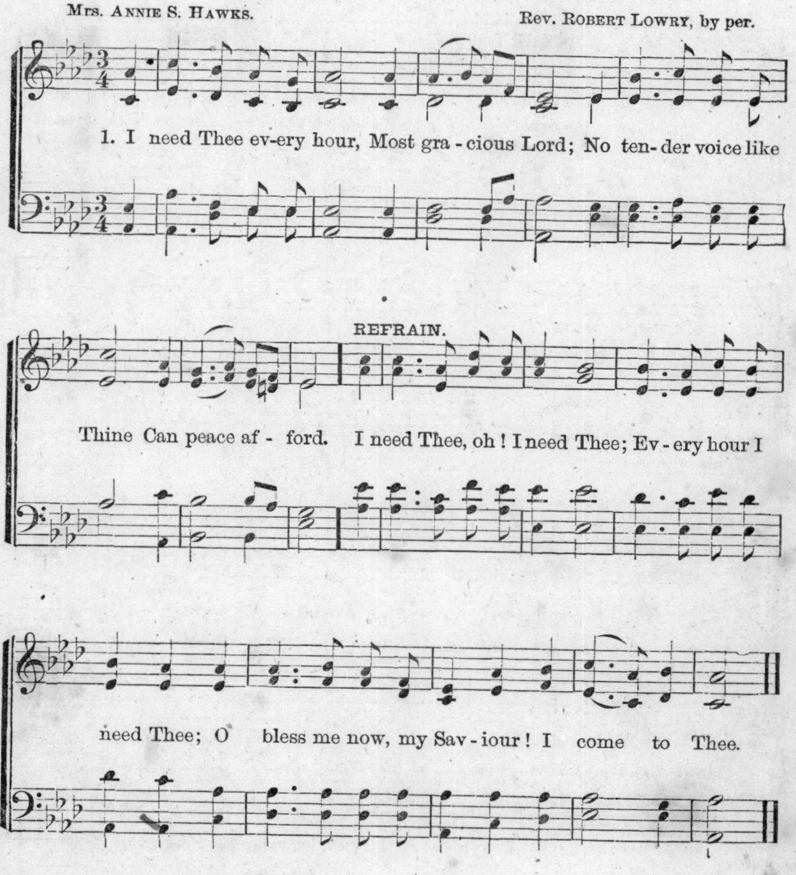

1. I need Thee ev-ery hour, Most gra - cious Lord; No ten-der voice like
Thine Can peace af - ford.
REFRAIN.
I need Thee, oh! I need Thee; Ev-ery hour I
need Thee; O bless me now, my Sav-iour! I come to Thee.

2 I need Thee every hour;
Stay Thou near by;
Temptations lose their power
When Thou art nigh. *Ref.*

3 I need Thee every hour,
In joy or pain:
Come quickly and abide,
Or life is vain. *Ref.*

4 I need Thee every hour;
Teach me Thy will:
And Thy rich promises
In me fulfil. *Ref.*

5 I need Thee every hour,
Most Holy One;
Oh, make me Thine indeed,
Thou blessed Son. *Ref.*

No. 4. Safe in the Arms of Jesus.

"Underneath are the everlasting arms."—DEUT. 33: 27.

FANNY J. CROSBY. W. H. DOANE, by per.

1. Safe in the arms of Je - sus, Safe on His gen - tle breast,
CHO.—Safe in the arms of Je - sus, Safe on His gen - tle breast,
rit.
END.
There by His love o'er-shad - ed, Sweet-ly my soul shall rest.
There by His love o'er-shad - ed, Sweet-ly my soul shall rest.
Hark! 'tis the voice of an - gels, Borne in a song to me,
D. C. Chorus.
O - ver the fields of glo - ry, O - ver the jas - per sea.....

2 Safe in the arms of Jesus,
Safe from corroding care,
Safe from the world's temptations,
Sin cannot harm me there.
Free from the blight of sorrow,
Free from my doubts and fears;
Only a few more trials,
Only a few more tears!—*Cho.*

3 Jesus, my heart's dear refuge,
Jesus has died for me;
Firm on the Rock of Ages
Ever my trust shall be.
Here let me wait with patience,
Wait till the night is o'er;
Wait till I see the morning
Break on the golden shore.—*Cho.*

No. 5. The Lord will Provide.

'Casting all your care upon Him, for He careth for you."—1 PETER, 5: 7.

Mrs. M. A. W. COOK. From "Hallowed Songs," by per.

1. In some way or oth - er the Lord will pro - vide: It may not be my way, It may not be thy way; And yet, in His own way, "The Lord will pro - vide."
2. At some time or oth - er the Lord will pro - vide: It may not be my time, It may not be thy time; And yet, in His own time, "The Lord will pro - vide."
CHORUS.
Then, we'll trust in the Lord, And He will pro - vide; Yes, we'll trust in the Lord, And He will pro - vide.

3 Despond then no longer: the Lord will provide;
And this be the token—
No word He hath spoken
Was ever yet broken:
"The Lord will provide."

4 March on then right boldly; the sea shall divide,
The pathway made glorious,
With shoutings victorious,
We'll join in the chorus,
"The Lord will provide."

No. 6. The Ninety and Nine.

"Rejoice with me, for I have found my sheep that was lost."—LUKE 15: 6.

ELIZABETH C. CLEPHANE. 1868. IRA D. SANKEY, by per.

1. There were ninety and nine that safe - ly lay In the shel - ter of the
fold, But one was out on the hills away, Far off from the gates of
gold— A - way on the mountains wild and bare, A-way from the tender
Shepherd's care, A - way from the ten - der Shepherd's care.

2.

"Lord, Thou hast here Thy ninety and nine:
Are they not enough for Thee?"
But the Shepherd made answer: "'T is of mine
Has wandered away from me;
And although the road be rough and steep
I go to the desert to find my sheep."

3.

But none of the ransomed ever knew
How deep were the waters crossed;
Nor how dark was the night that the Lord passed through
Ere He found His sheep that was lost.
Out in the desert He heard its cry—
Sick and helpless, and ready to die.

4.

"Lord, whence are those blood-drops all the way
That mark out the mountain's track?"
"They were shed for one who had gone astray
Ere the Shepherd could bring him back."
"Lord, whence are Thy hands so rent and torn?"
"They are pierced to-night by many a [thorn."

5.

But all thro' the mountains, thunder-riven,
And up from the rocky steep,
There rose a cry to the gate of heaven,
"Rejoice! I have found my sheep!"
And the angels echoed around the throne,
"Rejoice, for the Lord brings back His own!"

No. 7. We Shall Meet By and By.

"The ransomed of the Lord shall return and come to Zion with songs and everlasting joy upon their heads."—ISAIAH 30: 10.

Rev. JOHN ATKINSON. HUBERT P. MAIN, by per.

ff
pp
1. We shall meet be - yond the riv - er, By and by, by and by;
2. We shall strike the harps of glo - ry, By and by, by and by;
And the darkness shall be o - ver, By and by, by and by;
We shall sing redemption's sto - ry, By and by, by and by;
With the toil - some journey done, And the glorious bat - tle won,
And the strains for ev - er-more Shall re - sound in sweetness o'er
We shall shine forth as the sun, By and by, by and by.
Yon-der ev - er - last - ing shore, By and by, by and by.

We shall see and be like Jesus,
By and by, by and by;
Who a crown of life will give us,
By and by, by and by;
And the angels who fulfil
All the mandates of His will
Shall attend, and love us still,
By and by, by and by.

4 There our tears shall all cease flowing,
By and by, by and by;
And with sweetest rapture knowing,
By and by, by and by;
All the blest ones, who have gone
To the land of life and song,—
We with shoutings shall rejoin,
By and by, by and by.

No. 8. Jesus of Nazareth Passeth By.

"He heard that it was Jesus of Nazareth."—MARK 10: 47.

Miss ETA CAMPBELL. THEO. E. PERKINS, by per.

1. What means this ea - ger, anxious throng, Which moves with busy haste along—
2. Who is this Je - sus? Why should He The cit - y move so might-i - ly?
These wondrous gatherings day by day? What means this strange commotion pray?
A pass - ing stranger, has He skill To move the mul - ti - tude at will?
In accents hush'd the throng re-ply: "Je - sus of Naz - a - reth passeth by."
A - gain the stir - ring notes re-ply: "Je - sus of Naz - a - reth passeth by."
In accents hush'd the throng reply: "Je - sus of Naz-a - reth passeth by."
A - gain the stir ring notes re-ply: "Je - sus of Naz-a - reth passeth by."

Jesus of Nazareth.—Concluded.

3 Jesus! 'tis He who once below
Man's pathway trod, 'mid pain and woe;
And burdened ones, where'er He came,
Brought out their sick, and deaf, and lame
The blind rejoiced to hear the cry:
"Jesus of Nazareth passeth by."

4 Again He comes! From place to place
His holy footprints we can trace.
He pauseth at our threshold—nay,
He enters—condescends to stay.
Shall we not gladly raise the cry—
"Jesus of Nazareth passeth by?"

5 Ho! all ye heavy-laden come!
Here's pardon, comfort, rest, and home.
Ye wanderers from a Father's face,
Return, accept His proffered grace.
Ye tempted ones, there's refuge nigh:
"Jesus of Nazareth passeth by."

6 But if you still this call refuse,
And all His wondrous love abuse,
Soon will He sadly from you turn,
Your bitter prayer for pardon spurn.
"Too late! too late!" will be the cry—
"Jesus of Nazareth *has passed by.*"

No. 9.

Calling Now.

"To-day if ye will hear His voice, harden not your hearts."—HEB. 3:15.

P. P. BLISS. P. P. BLISS, by per.

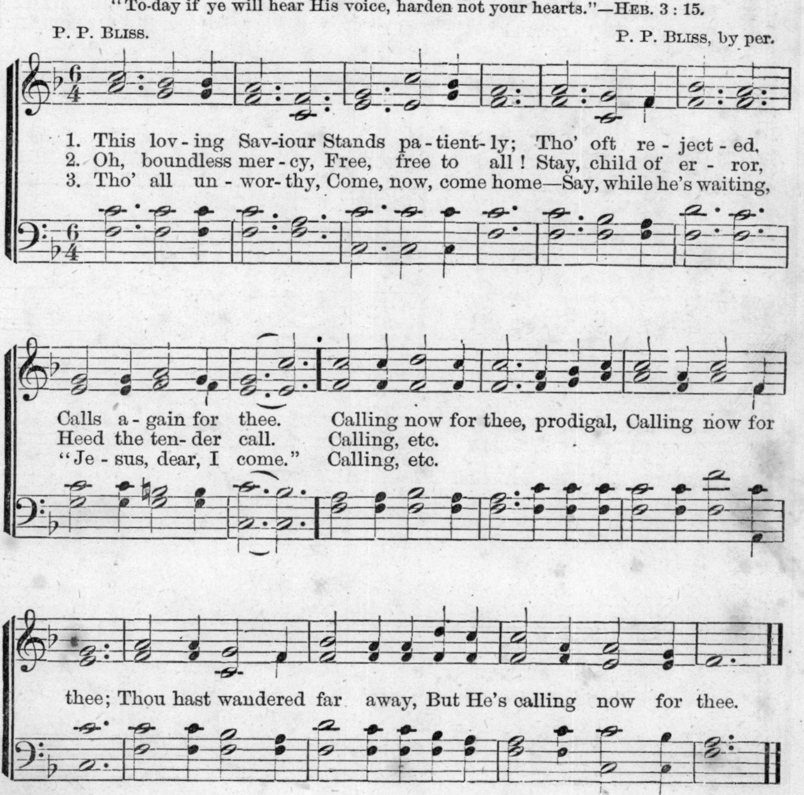
1. This lov-ing Sav-iour Stands pa-tient-ly; Tho' oft re-ject-ed,
2. Oh, boundless mer-cy, Free, free to all! Stay, child of er-ror,
3. Tho' all un-wor-thy, Come, now, come home—Say, while he's waiting,
Calls a-gain for thee. Calling now for thee, prodigal, Calling now for
Heed the ten-der call. Calling, etc.
"Je-sus, dear, I come." Calling, etc.
thee; Thou hast wandered far away, But He's calling now for thee.

No. 10. "Whosoever Will."

"Whosoever will, let him take the water of life freely."—Rev. 22: 17.

P. P. Bliss. P. P. Bliss, by per.

Joyfully.

1. "Who-so - ev - er heareth," shout, shout the sound! Send the blessed tidings all the world around; Spread the joy-ful news wher - ev - er man is found:
2. Who-so - ev - er com-eth, need not de - lay, Now the door is o - pen, en - ter while you may; Je - sus is the true, the on - ly Liv - ing Way:
3. "Who-so - ev - er will," the promise secure; "Whoso - ev - er will," for ev - er must en - dure; "Who-so - ev - er will," 'tis life for e - vermore:

CHORUS.

"Who-so - ev-er will, may come." "Who-so - ev - er will, who-so - ev - er will," Send the proc - la - ma - tion o - ver vale and hill; 'Tis a lov-ing Fa - ther calls the wand'rer home: "Who-so - ev - er will, may come."

No. 11. I Am Praying for You.

"Evening, and morning, and at noon, will I pray."—Psa. 55 : 17.

S. O'Maley Cluff. Ira D. Sankey, by per.

1. I have a Saviour, He's pleading in glo - ry, A dear, loving Saviour tho'
earth-friends be few; And now He is watching in ten - derness o'er me, And
oh that my Saviour were your Saviour too! For you I am praying, For
you I am praying, For you I am praying, I'm pray - ing for you.
CHORUS.
f
p
f
pp
rall.

2.
I have a Father: to me He has given
A hope for eternity, blessed and true;
And soon will He call me to meet Him in heaven,
But oh that He'd let me bring you with me too!

3.
I have a robe: 'tis resplendent in whiteness,
Awaiting in glory my wondering view;
Oh. when I receive it all shining in brightness,
Dear friend, could I see you receiving one too!

4.
I have a peace: it is calm as a river—
A peace that the friends of this world never knew;
My Saviour alone is its Author and Giver.
And oh, could I know it was given to you!

5.
When Jesus has found you, tell others the story,
That my loving Saviour is your Saviour too;
Then pray that your Saviour may bring them to glory,
And prayer will be answered—'twas answered for you!

No. 12. Where Are the Nine?

Read LUKE 17: 12-19.

P. P. BLISS. P. P. BLISS, by per.

Moderato.
1. Wand'ring a - far from the dwellings of men, Hear the sad cry of the
2. Loud - ly the stranger sang praise to the Lord, Knowing the cure had been
lep - ers—the ten; "Je - sus, have mer - cy!" brings healing di - vine;
wrought by His word, Grateful - ly own - ing the Heal - er Di - vine;
CHORUS.
One came to wor - ship, but where are the nine? Where are the nine?
Je - sus says ten - der - ly, "Where are the nine?"
Rit.
Where are the nine? Were there not ten cleansed? Where are the nine?

3 "Who is this Nazarene?" Pharisees say;
"Is He the Christ? tell us plainly, we pray."
Multitudes follow Him seeking a sign,
Show them His mighty works—Where are the nine?—*Cho.*

4 Jesus on trial to-day we can see,
Thousands deridingly ask, "Who is He?"
How they're rejecting Him, your Lord and mine!
Bring in the witnesses—Where are the nine?—*Cho.*

No. 13. That will be Heaven for Me.

"We know that, when He shall appear we shall be like Him; for we shall see Him as He is."—1 JOHN 3: 2.

P. P. BLISS. JAMES MCGRANAHAN, by per.

1. I know not the hour when my Lord will come To take me a-way to His own dear home; But I know that His presence will light-en the gloom, And that will be glo-ry for me.
2. I know not the song that the an-gels sing, I know not the sound of the harps' glad ring; But I know there'll be mention of Je-sus our King, And that will be mu-sic for me.
3. I know not the form of my man-sion fair, I know not the name that I then shall bear; But I know that my Sav-iour will wel-come me there, And that will be heav-en for me.

CHORUS.

And that will be glory for me,...... Oh, that will be glo-ry for me.....
And that will be music for me,...... Oh, that will be music for me.....
And that will be heaven for me,...... Oh, that will be heaven for me.....

Yes, that will be glory, oh, that will be glory for me....
Yes, that will be music, oh, that will be music for me....
Yes, that will be heaven, oh, that will be heaven for me..

Ritard.

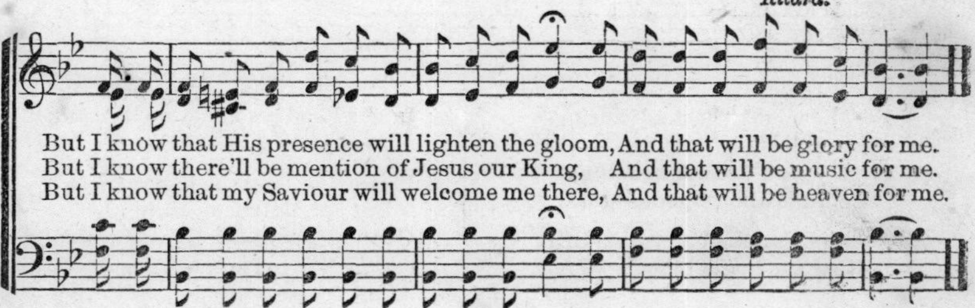

But I know that His presence will lighten the gloom, And that will be glory for me.
But I know there'll be mention of Jesus our King, And that will be music for me.
But I know that my Saviour will welcome me there, And that will be heaven for me.

No. 14. Hold the Fort.

"That which ye have, hold fast till I come."—Rev. 2 : 25.

P. P. Bliss. P. P. Bliss, by per.

1. Ho! my comrades, see the sig - nal Wav - ing in the sky!
Re - in - force - ments now ap - pear - ing, Vic - to - ry is nigh!
CHORUS.
"Hold the fort, for I am com - ing," Je - sus sig - nals still,
Wave the an - swer back to Hea - ven,—"By Thy grace we will."

2 See the mighty host advancing,
Satan leading on;
Mighty men around us falling,
Courage almost gone.—*Cho.*

3 See the glorious banner waving,
Hear the bugle blow.
In our Leader's name we'll triumph
Over every foe.—*Cho.*

4 Fierce and long the battle rages,
But our Help is near;
Onward comes our Great Commander,
Cheer, my comrades, cheer!—*Cho.*

No. 15. The Gate Ajar for Me.

"The gates of it shall not be shut at all by day; for there shall be no night there."—Rev. 21:25.

Mrs. Lydia Baxter. From "Hallowed Songs," by per.

1. There is a gate that stands a - jar, And through its portals gleaming,
A radiance from the Cross a - far, The Saviour's love re - veal - ing.
REFRAIN.
Oh, depth of mer - cy! can it be That gate was left a - jar for me?
For me, ... for me? . . . . Was left a - jar for me?
For me, for me?

2 That gate ajar stands free for all
Who seek through it salvation;
The rich and poor, the great and small,
Of every tribe and nation. *Ref.*

3 Press onward then, though foes may [frown,
While mercy's gate is open;
Accept the cross, and win the crown,
Love's everlasting token. *Ref.*

4 Beyond the river's brink we'll lay
The cross that here is given,
And bear the crown of life away,
And love Him more in heaven. *Ref.*

No. 16.

Once for All.

"Justified by His grace, through the redemption that is in Christ Jesus."—ROMANS 3 : 24.

P. P. BLISS. P. P. BLISS, by per.

1. Free from the law, oh, hap - py con - di - tion, Je - sus hath bled, and *there* is re - mis - sion; Curs'd by the law and bruised by the fall, Grace hath redeemed us once for all.

CHORUS.

Once for all, oh, sinner re - ceive it, Once for all, oh, brother, be - lieve it; Cling to the Cross, the bur - den will fall, Christ hath redeemed us once for all.

Once for all.—Concluded.

2 Now are we free—there's no condemnation,
Jesus provides a perfect salvation;
"Come unto *Me*," oh, hear His sweet call,
Come, and He saves us once for all.—*Cho.*

3 "Children of God," oh, glorious calling,
Surely His grace will keep us from falling;
Passing from death to life at His call,
Blessed salvation once for all.—*Cho.*

No. 17. Knocking, Knocking, Who is There?

"Behold, I stand at the door and knock; if any man hear My voice and open the door, I will come in to him and will sup with him, and he with Me."—Rev. 3: 20.

Mrs. H. B. Stowe, arr. Geo. F. Root, by per.

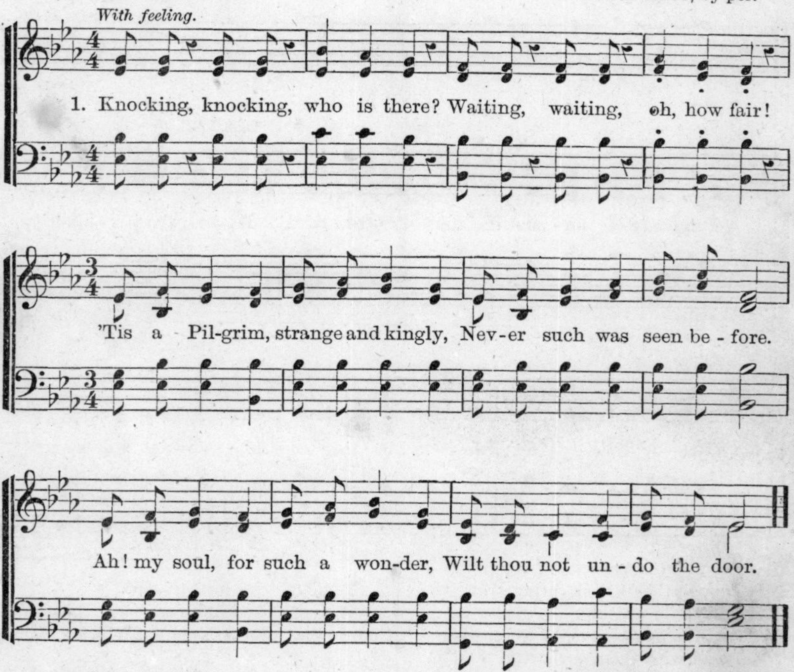

With feeling.
1. Knocking, knocking, who is there? Waiting, waiting, oh, how fair!
'Tis a Pil-grim, strange and kingly, Nev-er such was seen be - fore.
Ah! my soul, for such a won-der, Wilt thou not un - do the door.

2 Knocking, knocking, still He's there,
Waiting, waiting, wondrous fair;
But the door is hard to open,
For the weeds and ivy-vine,
With their dark and clinging tendrils,
Ever round the hinges twine.

3 Knocking, knocking—what still there?
Waiting, waiting, grand and fair;
Yes, the piercèd hand still knocketh,
And beneath the crowned hair
Beam the patient eyes, so tender,
Of thy Saviour, waiting there.

No. 18. Rescue the Perishing.

"Go out into the highways and hedges, and compel them to come in, that my house may be filled."—LUKE 14: 23.

FANNY J. CROSBY. W. H. DOANE, by per.

1. Res-cue the per-ish-ing, Care for the dying, Snatch them in pi - ty from
sin and the grave; Weep o'er the err - ing one, Lift up the fall - en,
CHORUS.
Tell them of Je - sus the migh-ty to save. Rescue the per - ish-ing,
Care for the dy - ing; Je - sus is mer - ci - ful, Je - sus will save.

2 Though they are slighting Him,
Still He is waiting,
Waiting the penitent child to receive.
Plead with them earnestly,
Plead with them gently:
He will forgive if they only believe.

3 Down in the human heart,
Crushed by the tempter,
Feelings lie buried that grace can restore:
Touched by a loving heart,
Wakened by kindness,
Chords that were broken will vibrate once more.

4 Rescue the perishing,
Duty demands it;
Strength for thy labor the Lord will provide:
Back to the narrow way
Patiently win them;
Tell the poor wanderer a Saviour has died.

No. 19. Ring the Bells of Heaven.

"There is joy in the presence of the angels of God over one sinner that repenteth."—LUKE 15: 10.

Rev. WM. O. CUSHING. GEO. F. ROOT, by per.

Joyfully.
1. Ring the bells of heav - en! there is joy to-day, For a soul re - turn-ing from the wild; See! the Father meets him out up-on the way, Wel-com-ing His wea-ry, wand'ring child.
2. Ring the bells of heav - en! there is joy to-day, For the wanderer now is re - con-ciled; Yes, a soul is res-cued from his sin-ful way, And is born a-new a ransomed child.
3. Ring the bells of heav - en! spread the feast to-day, An-gels, swell the glad triumphant strain! Tell the joy-ful tid-ings! bear it far a - way! For a precious soul is born a - gain.
CHORUS.
Glo - ry! glo - ry! how the an - gels sing; Glo - ry! glo - ry! how the loud harps ring; 'Tis the ransomed ar - my, like a mighty sea, Peal-ing forth the anthem of the free.

No. 20. Home of the Soul.

"In my Father's house are many mansions."—JOHN 14 : 2.

Mrs. ELLEN H. GATES. From "Hallowed Songs," by per.

1. I will sing you a song of that beau - ti - ful land,

The far a - way home of the soul, Where no storms ev - er

beat on the glit - ter-ing strand, While the years of e - ter - ni - ty

roll, While the years of e - ter - ni - ty roll; Where no storms ev - er

beat on the glit - ter-ing strand, While the years of e - ter - ni - ty roll.

Home of the Soul.—Concluded.

2 Oh, that home of the soul in my visions and dreams,
Its bright. jasper walls I can see;
Till I fancy but thinly the vail intervenes
‖: Between the fair city and me. :‖ Till I fancy, etc.

3 That unchangable home is for you and for me,
Where Jesus of Nazareth stands;
The King of all kingdoms forever, is He,
‖: And He holdeth our crowns in His hands. :‖ The King of, etc.

4 Oh, how sweet it will be in that beautiful land.
So free from all sorrow and pain;
With songs on our lips and with harps in our hands
‖: To meet one another again. :‖ With songs on, etc.

No. 21. What Hast Thou Done for Me?

"So Christ was once offered to bear the sins of many."—Heb. 9: 28.

Miss Frances R. Havergal. P. P. Bliss, by per.

Moderato.
1. I gave My life for thee, My pre-cious blood I shed,
2. My Fa-ther's house of light,— My glo-ry-cir-cled throne
That thou might'st ransomed be, And quickened from the dead;
I left, for earth-ly night, For wand'rings sad and lone;
f
I gave, I gave My life for thee, What hast thou given for Me?
I left, I left it all for thee, Hast thou left aught for Me?

3 I suffered much for thee,
More than thy tongue can tell,
Of bitterest agony,
To rescue thee from hell;
I've borne, I've borne it all for thee,
What hast thou borne for Me?

4 And I have brought to thee,
Down from My home above,
Salvation full and free,
My pardon and My love;
I bring, I bring rich gifts to thee,
What hast thou brought to Me?

No. 22. We're Going Home To-morrow.

"Willing rather to be absent from the body, and to be present with the Lord."—2 Cor. 5: 8.

Paulina. P. P. Bliss, by per.

1. We're going home, No more to roam, No more to sin and sor - row;
2. For wea - ry feet A - waits a street Of wondrous pave and gold-en;
No more to wear The brow of care—We're go - ing home to - mor-row.
For hearts that ache, The an - gels wake The sto - ry, sweet and old - en.
CHORUS.
We're go - - ing home, we're go - ing home to - mor-row;
We're go - ing home, we're going home, we're go - ing home to - mor-row;
We're go - - ing home, we're go - ing home to - morrow.
We're go - ing home, we're going home, we're go - ing home to - morrow.

3 For those who sleep,
And those who weep,
Above the portals narrow,
The mansions rise
Beyond the skies—
We're going home to-morrow.

4 Oh, joyful song!
Oh, ransomed throng!
Where sin no more shall sever;
Our King to see,
And, oh, to be
With Him at home forever!

No. 23.

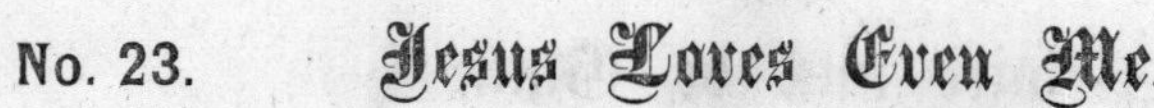
Jesus Loves Even Me.

"God is love."—1 JOHN 4: 8.

P. P. BLISS. P. P. BLISS, by per.

1. { I am so glad that our Father in heaven Tells of His love in the Book He has given,
Wonderful things in the Bible I see; This is the dearest, that Jesus loves me. }

CHORUS.

I am so glad that Jesus loves me, Jesus loves me, Jesus loves me, I am so glad that Jesus loves me, Jesus loves even me.......

2 Though I forget Him and wander away,
Still He doth love me wherever I stray;
Back to His dear loving arms would I flee,
When I remember that Jesus loves me.
I am so glad, etc.

3 Oh, if there's only one song I can sing,
When in His beauty I see the great King,
This shall my song in eternity be.
"Oh, what a wonder that Jesus loves me."
I am so glad, etc.

---

1 Jesus loves me, and I know I love Him,
Love brought Him down my poor soul to redeem:
Yes, it was love made Him die on the tree,
Oh, I am certain that Jesus loves me.
I am so glad, etc.

2 If one should ask of me, how could I tell?
Glory to Jesus, I know very well:
God's Holy Spirit with mine doth agree,
Constantly witnessing—Jesus loves me.
I am so glad, etc.

3 In this assurance I find sweetest rest,
Trusting in Jesus, I know I am blest;
Satan dismayed, from my soul now doth flee,
When I just tell him that Jesus loves me. I am so glad, etc.

No. 24. Rejoice and be Glad.

"The poor among men shall rejoice in the Holy One of Israel."—ISA. 29: 19.

Rev. HORATIUS BONAR. 1874. English Melody.

1. Re - joice and be glad! The Redeem-er has come! Go look on His cra - dle, His cross, and His tomb.
2. Re - joice and be glad! It is sunshine at last! The clouds have de - part - ed, the sha - dows are past.
3. Re - joice and be glad! For the blood hath been shed; Re - demption is fin - ished, the price hath been paid.
4. Re - joice and be glad! Now the pardon is free! The Just for the un - just has died on the tree.
5. Re - joice and be glad! For the Lamb that was slain O'er death is tri - umph-ant, and liv - eth a - gain.
6. Re - joice and be glad! For our King is on high, He pleadeth for us on His throne in the sky.
7. Re - joice and be glad! For He com - eth a - gain; He com - eth in glo - ry, the Lamb that was slain.

CHORUS.

Sound His prais - es, tell the Sto - ry, Of..... Him who was slain; Sound His prais - es, tell with glad - ness, He liv - eth a - gain.

(Cho. for 7th verse.)

Sound His prais - es, tell the Sto - ry, Of..... Him who was slain; Sound His prais - es, tell with glad - ness, He com - eth a - gain.

Words written for Messrs. M & S.

No. 25. Revive us Again.

(Tune on Page 26.)

"O Lord, revive Thy work."—HEB. 3: 2.

1 We praise Thee O God! for the Son of Thy love,
For Jesus who died, and is now gone above.
CHO.—Hallelujah! Thine the glory, Hallelujah! amen.
Hallelujah! Thine the glory, revive us again.

2 We praise Thee, O God! for Thy Spirit of light,
Who has shown us our Saviour, and scattered our night. *Cho.*

3 All glory and praise to the Lamb that was slain,
Who has borne all our sins, and cleansed every stain. *Cho.*

4 All glory and praise to the God of all grace,
Who has bought us; and sought us, and guided our ways. *Cho.*

5 Revive us again; fill each heart with Thy love;
May each soul be rekindled with fire from above. *Cho.*

REV. WM. PATON MACKEY, 1866.

No. 26. Something for Jesus.

"Lord, what wilt thou have me to do?"—ACTS 9: 6.

REV. S. D. PHELPS, D. D. REV. R. LOWRY, by per.

1. Sav - iour! Thy dy - ing love Thou gavest me, Nor should I aught with-hold, Dear Lord, from Thee; In love my soul would bow, My heart ful - fill its vow, Some offering bring Thee now, Something for Thee.
2. At the blest mer - cy - seat, Pleading for me, My fee - ble faith looks up, Je - sus, to Thee: Help me the cross to bear, Thy wondrous love declare, Some song to raise, or prayer, Something for Thee.
3. Give me a faith - ful heart— Like-ness to Thee— That each de - part - ing day Henceforth may see Some work of love be - gun, Some deed of kindness done, Some wand'rer sought and won, Something for Thee.
4. All that I am and have— Thy gifts so free— In joy, in grief, through life, Dear Lord, for Thee! And when Thy face I see, My ransomed soul shall be, Through all e - ter - ni - ty, Something for Thee.

No. 27. Pass Me Not.

"Whosoever shall call upon the name of the Lord shall be saved."—Acts 2: 21.

Fanny J. Crosby, 1868. W. H. Doane, by per.

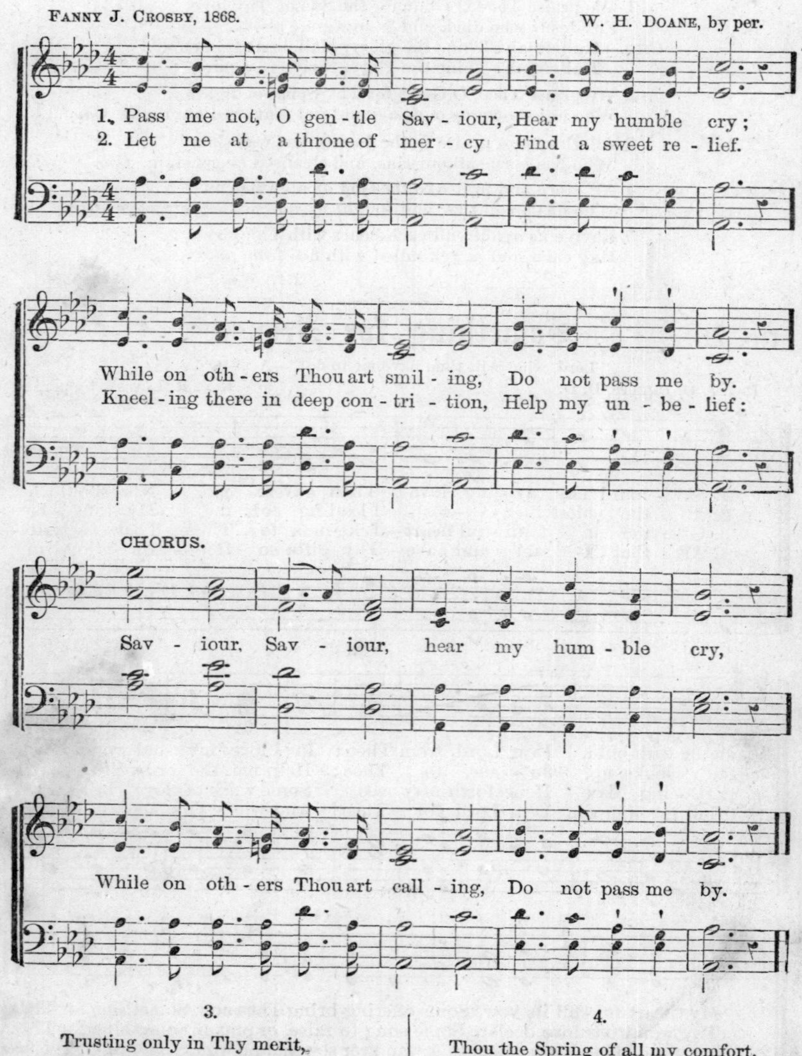
1. Pass me not, O gen-tle Sav-iour, Hear my humble cry;
2. Let me at a throne of mer-cy Find a sweet re-lief.
While on oth-ers Thou art smil-ing, Do not pass me by.
Kneel-ing there in deep con-tri-tion, Help my un-be-lief:
CHORUS.
Sav-iour, Sav-iour, hear my hum-ble cry,
While on oth-ers Thou art call-ing, Do not pass me by.

3.

Trusting only in Thy merit,
Would I seek Thy face;
Heal my wounded, broken spirit,
Save me by Thy grace. *Cho.*

4.

Thou the Spring of all my comfort,
More than life to me,
Whom have I on earth beside Thee?
Whom in Heaven but Thee? *Cho.*

No. 28. One more Day's Work for Jesus.

"I must work the works of HIM that sent Me, while it is day."—JOHN 9: 4.

Miss ANNA WARNER. Rev. ROBERT LOWRY, by per.

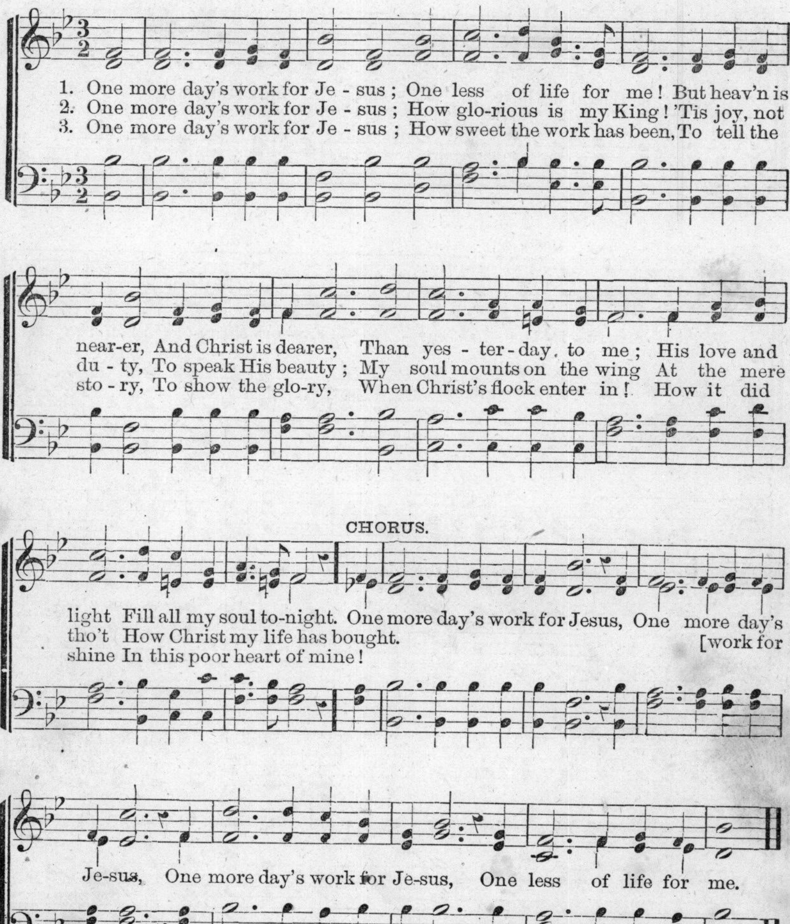

1. One more day's work for Je - sus ; One less of life for me ! But heav'n is
2. One more day's work for Je - sus ; How glo-rious is my King ! 'Tis joy, not
3. One more day's work for Je - sus ; How sweet the work has been, To tell the
near-er, And Christ is dearer, Than yes - ter-day. to me ; His love and
du - ty, To speak His beauty ; My soul mounts on the wing At the mere
sto - ry, To show the glo-ry, When Christ's flock enter in ! How it did
CHORUS.
light Fill all my soul to-night. One more day's work for Jesus, One more day's
tho't How Christ my life has bought. [work for
shine In this poor heart of mine !
Je-sus, One more day's work for Je-sus, One less of life for me.

4 One more day's work for Jesus—
Oh yes, a weary day;
But heaven shines clearer,
And rest comes nearer,
At each step of the way;
And Christ in all—
Before His face I fall.—*Cho.*

5 Oh, blessed work for Jesus!
Oh, rest at Jesus' feet!
There toil seems pleasure.
My wants are treasure,
And pain for Him is sweet.
Lord, if I may,
I'll serve another day.—*Cho.*

No. 29. What a Friend We Have in Jesus.

"There is a Friend that sticketh closer than a brother."—PROV. 18: 24.

. REV. H. BONAR. CHARLES C. CONVERSE, by per.

1. What a friend we have in Je - sus, All our sins and griefs to bear;
What a priv - i - lege to car - ry Ev - ery thing to God in prayer.
Oh, what peace we oft - en for - feit, Oh, what needless pain we bear—
All because we do not car - ry Ev - ery thing to God in prayer.

2 Have we trials and temptations?
Is there trouble anywhere?
We should never be discouraged,
Take it to the Lord in prayer.
Can we find a Friend so faithful,
Who will all our sorrows share?
Jesus knows our every weakness,
Take it to the Lord in prayer.

3 Are we weak and heavy laden,
Cumbered with a load of care?
Precious Saviour, still our refuge,—
Take it to the Lord in prayer.
Do thy friends despise, forsake thee?
Take it to the Lord in prayer;
In His arms He'll take and shield thee,
Thou wilt find a solace there.

No. 30. Wondrous Love.

"God so loved the world."—John 3: 16.

Mrs. M. Stockton. Wm. G. Fischer, by per.

1. God loved the world of sin - ners lost And ru - ined by the
fall; Sal - va - tion full, at highest cost, He of - fers free to all.
CHORUS.
Oh, 'twas love, 'twas wondrous love! The love of God to me; It
brought my Saviour from a - bove, To die on Cal - va - ry.

2 E'en now by faith I claim Him mine,
The risen Son of God;
Redemption by His death I find,
And cleansing through the blood.

3 Love brings the glorious fulness in,
And to His saints makes known
The blessed rest from inbred sin,
Through faith in Christ alone.

4 Believing souls, rejoicing go;
There shall to you be given
A glorious foretaste, here below,
Of endless life in heaven.

5 Of victory now o'er Satan's power
Let all the ransomed sing,
And triumph in the dying hour
Through Christ the Lord our King.

No. 31. "More to Follow."

"Bring me yet a vessel."—2 KINGS 4 : 6.

P. P. BLISS. P. P. BLISS, by per.

1. Have you on the Lord believed? Still there's more to fol - low;
2. Have you felt the Sav-iour near? Still there's more to fol - low;
3. Have you felt the Spirit's power? Still there's more to fol - low:
Of His grace have you received? Still there's more to fol - low;
Does His bless - ed presence cheer? Still there's more to fol - low;
Fall - ing like the gen - tle shower? Still there's more to fol - low;
Oh, the grace the Fa-ther shows! Still there's more to fol - low,
Oh, the love that Je - sus shows! Still there's more to fol - low,
Oh, the power the Spir - it shows! Still there's more to fol - low,
Free - ly He His grace bestows, Still there's more to fol - low.
Free - ly He His love bestows, Still there's more to fol - low.
Free - ly He His power bestows, Still there's more to fol - low.
CHORUS.
More and more, more and more, Al - ways more to fol - low,

"More to Follow."—Concluded.

Oh, His matchless, boundless love! Still there's more to fol-low.

No. 32. Bless Me Now.

"Behold, now is the accepted time; behold, now is the day o salvation."—2 Cor. 6: 2.

Rev. Alexander Clark. Rev. Robert Lowry, by per.

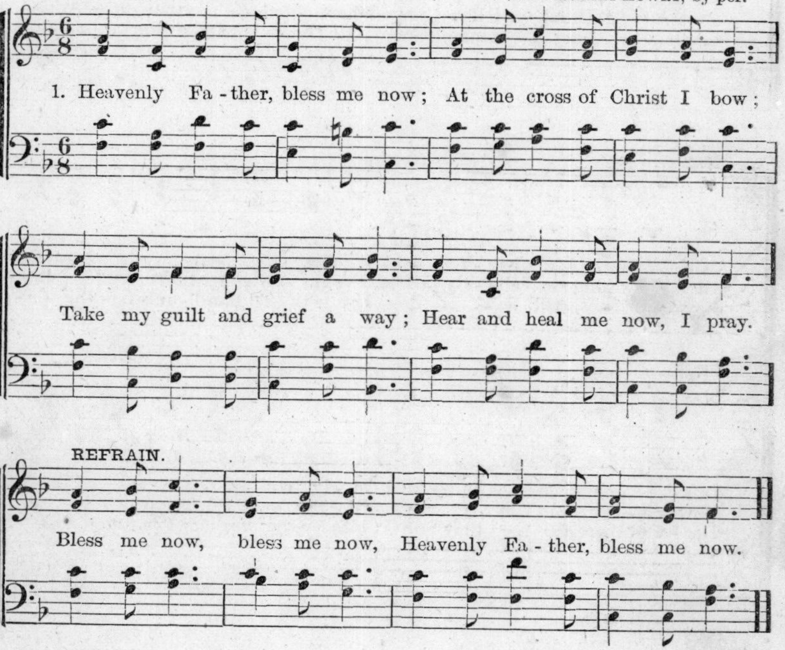

1. Heavenly Fa-ther, bless me now; At the cross of Christ I bow;
Take my guilt and grief a way; Hear and heal me now, I pray.

REFRAIN.

Bless me now, bless me now, Heavenly Fa-ther, bless me now.

2 Now, O Lord! this very hour,
Send Thy grace and show Thy power;
While I rest upon Thy word,
Come and bless me now, O Lord! *Ref.*

3 Now, just now, for Jesus' sake,
Lift the clouds, the fetters break;
While I look, and as I cry,
Touch and cleanse me ere I die. *Ref.*

4 Never did I so adore
Jesus Christ, thy Son, before;
Now the time! and this the place!
Gracious Father, show Thy grace. *Ref.*

No. 33. Where Hast Thou Gleaned To-day?

"The field is the world * * * and the reapers are the angels"—Matt. 13: 38.

P. P. Bliss.
P. P. Bliss, by per.
Question.
1. Wea-ry gleaner, whence comest thou, With empty hands and clouded brow?
2. Careless gleaner, what hast thou here, These faded flow'rs and leaf-lets sere?
3. Burden'd gleaner, thy sheaves I see; In - deed thou must a-wea - ry be!
Plodding a - long thy lone - ly way, Tell me, where hast thou glean'd to-day?
Hungry and thirst - y, tell me, pray, Where, oh, where hast thou glean'd to-day?
Singing a - long the homeward way, Glad one, where hast thou glean'd to-day?
Answer.
Late I found a bar - ren field, The har - vest past my search revealed,
All day long in sha - dy bow'rs, I've gai - ly sought earth's fairest flow'rs;
Stay me not, till day is done I've gath-er'd hand - fuls one by one;
Oth - ers golden sheaves had gained, On - ly stub- ble for me re - mained.
Now, a - las! too late I see All I've gather'd is van - i - ty.
Here and there for me they fall, Close by the reapers I've found them all.
CHORUS.
Forth to the har-vest field a - way! Gather your hand-fuls while you may;

Where Hast Thou Gleaned?—Concluded.

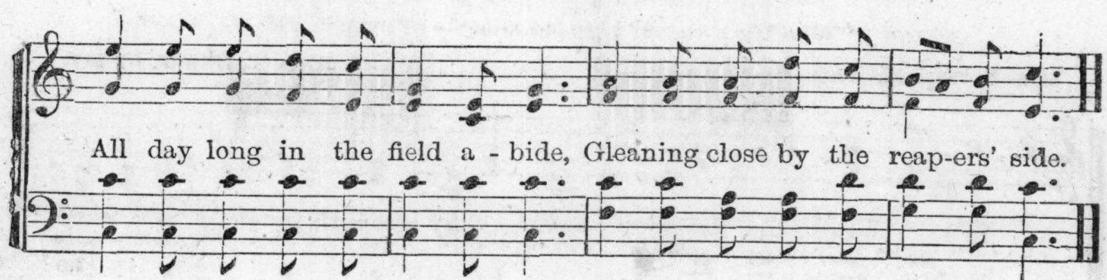
All day long in the field a - bide, Gleaning close by the reap-ers' side.

No. 36. Ah, My Heart.

Come unto Me, all ye that labor and are heavy laden."—MATT. 11: 28.

Tr. JOHN M. NEALE. P. P. BLISS, by per.

1st SOLO.
1. Ah, my heart is heav-y la - den, Wea - ry and op-pressed!

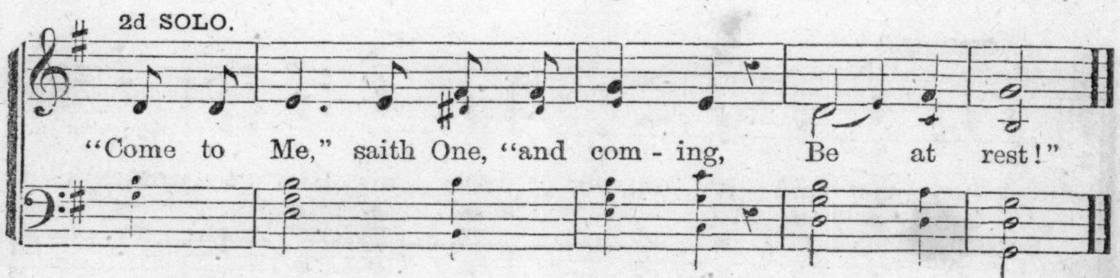
2d SOLO.
"Come to Me," saith One, "and com - ing, Be at rest!"

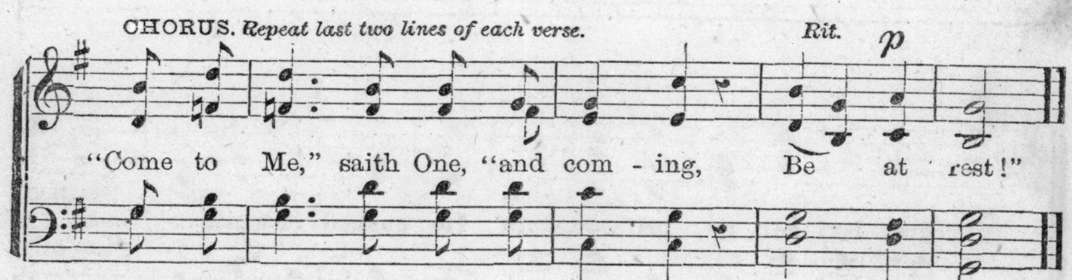
CHORUS. Repeat last two lines of each verse.
Rit.
p
"Come to Me," saith One, "and com - ing, Be at rest!"

2 Hath He marks to lead me to Him,
If He be my Guide?
"In His feet and hands are wound-prints,
And His side."—*Cho.*

3 Is there diadem, as monarch,
That His brow adorns?
"Yes, a crown in very surety,
But of thorns!"—*Cho.*

4 If I find Him, if I follow,
What's my portion here?
"Many a sorrow, many a conflict,
Many a tear."—*Cho.*

5 If I still hold closely to Him,
What have I at last?
"Sorrow vanquished, labor ended,
Jordan past!"—*Cho.*

6 If I ask Him to receive me,
Will He say me nay?
"Not till earth and not till heaven
Pass away!"—*Cho.*

No. 35. All to Christ I Owe.

"Who His own self bare our sins."—1 PETER 2: 24.

Mrs. ELVINA M. HALL. JOHN T. GRAPE, by per.

1. I hear the Sav-iour say, Thy strength in-deed is small;
Child of weakness, watch and pray, Find in Me thine all in all.
CHORUS.
Je-sus paid it all, All to Him I owe;
Sin had left a crimson stain: He washed it white as snow.

2 Lord, now indeed I find
Thy power, and Thine alone,
Can change the leper's spots,
And melt the heart of stone.—*Cho.*

3 For nothing good have I
Whereby Thy grace to claim—
I'll wash my garment white
In the blood of Calvary's Lamb.—*Cho.*

4 When from my dying bed
My ransomed soul shall rise,
Then "Jesus paid it all"
Shall rend the vaulted skies.—*Cho.*

5 And when before the throne
I stand in Him complete,
I'll lay my trophies down,
All down at Jesus' feet.—*Cho.*

No. 36. Oh, how He Loves.

"A Friend that sticketh closer than a brother."—Prov. 18: 24.

Miss Marianne Nunn. Hubert P. Main, by per.

1. One there is a - bove all others, Oh, how He loves! His is love be-
2. 'Tis e - ter - nal life to know Him, Oh, how He loves! Think, oh, think how
yond a brother's, Oh, how He loves! Earth - ly friends may
much we owe Him, Oh, how He loves! With His pre - cious
fail or leave us, One day soothe, the next day grieve us;
blood He bought us, In the wil - der - ness He sought us,
But this Friend will ne'er de - ceive us, Oh, how He loves!
To His fold He safe - ly brought us Oh, how He loves!

3.

Blessed Jesus! would you know Him,
Oh, how He loves!
Give yourselves entirely to Him,
Oh, how He loves!
Think no longer of the morrow,
From the past new courage borrow,
Jesus carries all your sorrow,
Oh, how He loves!

4.

All your sins shall be forgiven,
Oh, how He loves!
Backward shall your foes be driven,
Oh, how He loves!
Best of blessings He'll provide you,
Nought but good shall e'er betide you,
Safe to glory He will guide you,
Oh, how He loves!

No. 37. Tell Me the Old, Old Story.

"Tell them how great things the Lord hath done."—MARK 5: 19.

Miss KATE HANKEY. W. H. DOANE, by per.

1. Tell me the Old, Old Sto-ry, Of un-seen things a-bove, Of
2. Tell me the Sto-ry slow-ly, That I may take it in— That
Je-sus and His glo-ry, Of Je-sus and His love. Tell me the Sto-ry
wonder-ful re-demp-tion, God's rem-e-dy for sin. Tell me the Sto-ry
sim-ply, As to a lit-tle child, For I am weak and wea-ry, And
oft-en, For I for-get so soon, The "early dew" of morn-ing Has
CHORUS.
help-less and de-filed. Tell me the Old, Old Sto-ry, Tell me the Old, Old
passed a-way at noon.
Sto-ry, Tell me the Old, Old Sto-ry Of Je-sus and His love.

Tell Me the Old, Old Story.—Concluded.

3 Tell me the story softly,
With earnest tones, and grave:
Remember! I'm the sinner
Whom Jesus came to save,
Tell me that story always,
If you would really be,
In any time of trouble,
A comforter to me.

4 Tell me the same old story,
When you have cause to fear
That this world's empty glory
Is costing me too dear.
Yes, and when that world's glory
Is dawning on my soul,
Tell me the old, old story:
"Christ Jesus makes thee whole."

No. 38. The Prodigal Child.

"I will arise, and go to my father."—LUKE 15: 18.

Mrs. ELLEN H. GATES. W. H. DOANE, by per.

1. Come home! come home! You are wea-ry at heart, For the way has been
2. Come home! come home! For we watch and we wait, And we stand at the
dark, And so lone-ly and wild. O prod-i-gal child! Come
gate, While the shadows are piled. O prod-i-gal child! Come
CHORUS.
rit.
home! oh come home! Come home! Come, oh come home!
home! oh come home! Come home! Come, oh come home, come home!
Come home, come home!

3 Come home! come home!
From the sorrow and blame,
From the sin and the shame,
And the tempter that smiled,
O prodigal child!
Come home, oh come home!

4 Come home! come home!
There is bread and to spare,
And a warm welcome there,
Then, to friends reconciled,
O prodigal child!
Come home, oh, come home!

No. 39. I Love to Tell the Story.

"I will speak of Thy wondrous work."—PSAL. 145: 5.

MISS KATE HANKEY, 1867. W. G. FISCHER, by per.

1. I love to tell the Sto-ry Of unseen things above, Of Je - sus and His Glo-ry Of Je - sus and His Love! I love to tell the Sto - ry! Be-cause I know it's true; It sat-isfies my longings, As nothing else would do.
2. I love to tell the Sto-ry! More wonderful it seems, Than all the golden fan-cies Of all our golden dreams. I love to tell the Sto - ry! It did so much for me! And that is just the reason, I tell it now to thee.
CHORUS.
I love to tell the Sto - ry! 'Twill be my theme in glo - ry,
To tell the Old, Old Sto - ry Of Je - sus and His love.

I Love to Tell the Story.—Concluded.

3 I love to tell the Story!
'Tis pleasant to repeat
What seems, each time I tell it,
More wonderfully sweet.
I love to tell the Story;
For some have never heard
The message of salvation
From God's own Holy Word.

4 I love to tell the Story!
For those who know it best
Seem hungering and thirsting
To hear it, like the rest.
And when, in scenes of glory,
I sing the NEW, NEW SONG,
'Twill be—the OLD, OLD STORY
That I have loved so long.

No. 40. Holy Spirit, Faithful Guide.

"I will guide thee with mine eye."—PSALM 32: 8.

M. M. WELLS, 1858. M. M. WELLS, by per.

1. Ho - ly Spir - it, faith - ful guide, Ev - er near the Chris-tian's side;
FINE.
Gent-ly lead us by the hand, Pil-grims in a des - ert land;
D. C. Whisp'ring softly, wanderer come! Fol-low me, I'll guide thee home.
D. C.
Wea-ry souls for e'er re - joice, While they hear that sweetest voice

2 Ever present, truest Friend,
Ever near Thine aid to lend,
Leave us not to doubt and fear,
Groping on in darkness drear,
When the storms are raging sore,
Hearts grow faint, and hopes give o'er,
Whispering softly, wanderer come!
Follow me, I'll guide thee home.

3 When our days of toil shall cease,
Waiting still for sweet release,
Nothing left but heaven and prayer,
Wond'ring if our names were there;
Wading deep the dismal flood,
Pleading nought but Jesus' blood;
Whispering softly, wanderer come!
Follow me, I'll guide thee home!

No. 41. The Light of the World is Jesus.

"I am the light of the world."—JOHN 9: 5.

P. P. BLISS. P. P. BLISS, by per.

1. The whole world was lost in the dark-ness of sin; The Light of the world is Je - sus. Like sun-shine at noon-day His glo - ry shone in, The Light of the world is Je - sus.
2. No dark-ness have we who in Je-sus a - bide, The Light of the world is Je - sus. We walk in the Light when we fol - low our Guide, The Light of the world is Je - sus.
3. Ye dwell-ers in dark-ness with sin-blind-ed eyes, The Light of the world is Je - sus. Go, wash, at His bid - ding, and light will a - rise, The Light of the world is Je - sus.
4. No need of the sun-light in heav-en, we're told, The Light of that world is Je - sus. The Lamb is the light in the Cit - y of Gold, The Light of that world is Je - sus.

CHORUS.

Come to the Light, 'tis shining for thee; Sweetly the Light has dawn'd upon me,

The Light of the World.—Concluded.

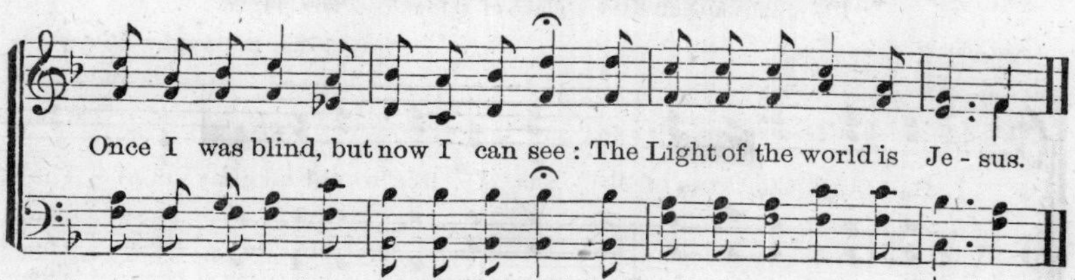
Once I was blind, but now I can see : The Light of the world is Je - sus.

No. 42. The Holy Spirit.

Three warnings : Resist not, Grieve not, Quench not.

P. P. BLISS. P. P. BLISS, by per.

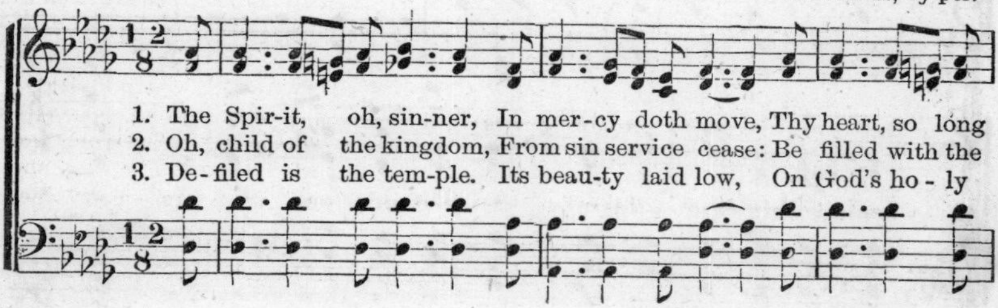

1. The Spir-it, oh, sin-ner, In mer-cy doth move, Thy heart, so long
2. Oh, child of the kingdom, From sin service cease: Be filled with the
3. De-filed is the tem-ple. Its beau-ty laid low, On God's ho-ly

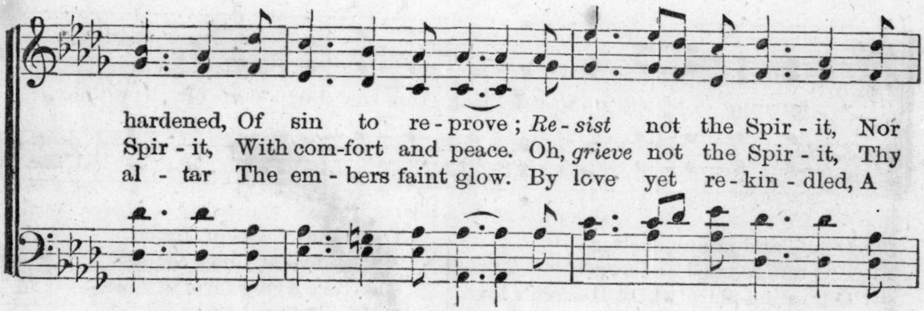

hardened, Of sin to re-prove ; *Re-sist* not the Spir - it, Nor
Spir - it, With com-fort and peace. Oh, *grieve* not the Spir - it, Thy
al - tar The em - bers faint glow. By love yet re-kin - dled, A

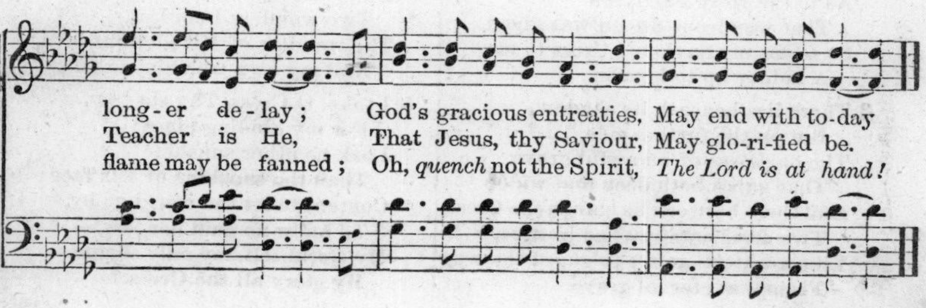

long-er de-lay ; God's gracious entreaties, May end with to-day
Teacher is He, That Jesus, thy Saviour, May glo-ri-fied be.
flame may be fanned ; Oh, *quench* not the Spirit, *The Lord is at hand !*

No. 43. The Cross of Jesus.

"His children shall have a place of refuge."—Prov. 14: 26.

Miss E. C. Clephane. Ira. D. Sankey, by per.

p
1. Be - neath the Cross of Je - sus I fain would take my stand— The
sha - dow of a mighty Rock, With-in a wea - ry land. A
home within the wilderness, A rest up - on the way, From the
burning of the noon-tide heat, And the bur - den of the day.

2 O safe and happy shelter,
O refuge tried and sweet,
O trysting-place where Heaven's love,
And Heaven's justice meet!
As to the Holy Patriarch
That wondrous dream was given,
So seems my Saviour's Cross to me,
A ladder up to heaven.

3 There lies beneath its shadow,
But on the further side,
The darkness of an awful grave
That gapes both deep and wide;
And there between us stands the Cross,
Two arms outstretched to save,
Like a watchman set to guard the way
From that eternal grave.

4 Upon that Cross of Jesus,
Mine eye at times can see
The very dying form of One,
Who suffered there for me
And from my smitten heart with tears
Two wonders I confess,—
The wonders of His glorious love,
And my own worthlessness.

5 I take, O Cross, Thy shadow,
For my abiding place;
I ask no other sunshine
Than the sunshine of His face:
Content to let the world go by,
To know no gain nor loss,—
My sinful self, my only shame,—
My glory all the Cross.

No. 44. The New Song.

"And they sung as it were a new song before the throne."—Rev. 14: 3.

Rev. A. T. Pierson. P. P. Bliss, by per.

Allegretto.
1. With harps and with vi - ols, there stand a great throng
In the pre - sence of Je - sus, and sing this new song:—
CHORUS.
Un - to Him who hath loved us and washed us from
sin, Un - to Him be the glo - ry for ev - er. A - men.

2 All these once were sinners, defiled in His sight,
Now arrayed in pure garments in praise they unite.—*Cho.*

3 He maketh the rebel a priest and a king.
He hath bought us and taught us this new song to sing.—*Cho.*

4 How helpless and hopeless we sinners had been,
If He never had loved us till cleansed from our sin.—*Cho.*

5 Aloud in His praises our voices shall ring,
So that others believing, this new song shall sing.—*Cho*

No. 45. Near the Cross.

"Peace through the blood of His cross."—COLL. 1: 29.

FANNY J. CROSBY. W. H. DOANE, by per.

1. Je - sus, keep me near the cross, There a pre-cious fountain
2. Near the cross, a trembling soul, Love and mer - cy found me;
Free to all— a heal - ing stream, Flows from Calvary's mountain.
There the bright and morn- ing star Shed its beams a - round me.
CHORUS.
In the Cross, in the Cross, Be my glo - ry ev - er;
Till my rap - tured soul shall find Rest beyond the riv - er.

3 Near the Cross! O Lamb of God,
Bring its scenes before me;
Help me walk from day to day,
With its shadows o'er me. *Cho.*

4 Near the Cross I'll watch and wait,
Hoping, trusting ever,
Till I reach the golden strand,
Just beyond the river. *Cho.*

No. 46. Oh, Sing of His Mighty Love.

"Mighty to save."—ISAIAH 63: 1.

REV. FRANK BOTTOME, D. D. 1869. WM. B. BRADBURY, by per.

1. Oh, bliss of the pu-ri-fied, bliss of the free, I plunge in the crimson tide o-pen'd for me; O'er sin and un-cleanness ex-ult-ing I stand, And point to the print of the nails in His hand.
2. Oh, bliss of the pu-ri-fied, Je-sus is mine, No longer in dread-condem-na-tion I pine; In conscious sal-va-tion I sing of His grace, Who lift-eth up-on me the light of His face.
CHORUS.
Oh, sing of His mighty love, Sing of His mighty love, Sing of His mighty love, Mighty to save.
Rit.

3 Oh, bliss of the purified! bliss of the pure!
No wound hath the soul that His blood cannot cure;
No sorrow-bowed head but may sweetly find rest,
No tears but may dry them on Jesus' breast. *Cho.*

4 O Jesus the crucified! Thee will I sing,
My blessed Redeemer, my God and my King;
My soul, filled with rapture, shall shout o'er the grave,
And triumph in death in the "Mighty to Save." *Cho.*

No. 47. Not Now, My Child.

"Oh, that I had wings like a dove, for then would I fly away, and be at rest."—PSALM 4: 6.

MRS. CATHERINE PENNEFATHER. 1863. IRA D. SANKEY, by per.

Slow, and with expression.
1. Not now, my child,— a lit - tle more rough toss - ing, A lit - tle lon - ger on the bil-lows' foam; A few more journeyings in the des - ert darkness, And then, the sun-shine of thy Fa-ther's Home!
2. Not now; for I have wanderers in the dis - tance, And thou must call them in with pa-tient love; Not now, for I have sheep up-on the mountains, And thou must fol-low them where'er they rove.

3 Not now; for I have loved ones sad and weary;
Wilt thou not cheer them with a kindly smile?
Sick ones, who need thee in their lonely sorrow;
Wilt thou not tend them yet a little while?

4 Not now: for wounded hearts are sorely bleeding,
And thou must teach those widowed hearts to sing:
Not now; for orphans' tears are quickly falling,
They must be gathered 'neath some sheltering wing.

5 Go, with the name of Jesus, to the dying,
And speak that Name in all its living power;
Why should thy fainting heart grow chill and weary?
Canst thou not watch with Me one little hour?

6 One little hour! and then the glorious crowning,
The golden harp-strings, and the victor's palm;
One little hour! and then the hallelujah!
Eternity's long, deep, thanksgiving psalm!

No. 48. Every Day and Hour.

"Cleanse me from my sin."—Ps. 51: 2.

FANNY J. CROSBY. W. H DOANE, by per.

Slowly.
1. Saviour, more than life to me, I am clinging, clinging close to Thee;
2. Thro' this changing world below, Lead me gently, gently as I go;
Let Thy precious blood ap-plied, Keep me ev-er, ev-er near Thy side.
Trusting Thee, I can-not stray, I can never, never lose my way.
REFRAIN.
Ev - ery day, ev - ery hour, Let me
Ev - ery day and hour, ev - ery day and hour,
feel Thy cleansing power; May Thy ten - der love to me Bind me
clos-er, clos-er, Lord, to Thee.

3

Let me love Thee more and more,
Till this fleeting, fleeting life is o'er;
Till my soul is lost in love,
In a brighter, brighter world above.

Ref. Every day and hour, &c.

No. 49. The Wondrous Gift.

"By grace are ye saved."—EPH. 2: 8.

DR. PHILIP DODDRIDGE. IRA D. SANKEY, by per.

1. Grace! 'tis a charming sound, Har-mo-nious to the ear; Heaven
with the ech-o shall resound, And all the earth shall hear.
REFRAIN.
Saved by grace a-lone, This is all my plea;
Je-sus died for all mankind, And Je-sus died for me.

2 Grace first contrived a way
To save rebellious man;
And all the steps that grace display,
Which drew the wondrous plan. *Ref.*

3 Grace taught my roving feet
To tread the heavenly road;
And new supplies each hour I meet,
While pressing on to God. *Ref.*

4 Grace all the work shall crown,
Through everlasting days;
It lays in heaven the topmost stone,
And well deserves our praise. *Ref.*

No. 50. Precious Promise.

"Whereby are given unto us exceeding great and precious promises."—2 PET. 1: 4.

Words by N. N.
P. P. BLISS, by per.
1. Pre - cious promise God hath giv - en To the wea - ry pass - er by,
2. When temp - ta - tions al - most win thee, And thy trusted watchers fly,
On the way from earth to heaven, "I will guide thee with Mine eye."
Let this promise ring with - in thee, "I will guide thee with Mine eye."
REFRAIN.
I will guide thee, I will guide thee, I will guide thee with Mine eye;
On the way from earth to heaven, I will guide thee with Mine eye.

3 When thy secret hopes have perished,
In the grave of years gone by,
Let this promise still be cherished,
"I will guide thee with Mine eye."

4 When the shades of life are falling,
And the hour has come to die,
Hear thy trusty Pilot calling,
"I will guide thee with Mine eye."

He Leadeth Me.

No. 51.

"He leadeth me by the still waters."—PSALM 23: 2.

Rev. JOS. H. GILMORE. 1861.

WM. B. BRADBURY, by per.

1. He leadeth me! oh! blessed thought, Oh! words with heav'nly comfort fraught;
2. Sometimes 'mid scenes of deepest gloom, Sometimes where Eden's bowers bloom,
What-e'er I do, wher-e'er I be, Still 'tis God's hand that lead-eth me.
By wa-ters still, o'er troubled sea,—Still 'tis His hand that lead-eth me.
REFRAIN.
He lead-eth me! He lead-eth me! By His own hand He leadeth me;
His faithful follower I would be, For by His hand He lead-eth me.

3 Lord, I would clasp Thy hand in mine,
Nor ever murmur nor repine—
Content, whatever lot I see,
Since 'tis my God that leadeth me.—*Ref.*

And when my task on earth is done,
When, by Thy grace, the victory's won,
E'en death's cold wave I will not flee,
Since God through Jordan leadeth me.—*Ref.*

No. 52. When Jesus Comes.

"Unto them that look for Him shall He appear the second time, without sin, unto salvation."—HEB. 9 : 28.

P. P. BLISS. P. P. BLISS, by per.

1. Down life's dark vale we wander, Till Jesus comes; We watch and wait and wonder, Till Je- sus comes.
2. Oh, let my lamp be burning When Jesus comes; For Him my soul be yearning, When Je- sus comes.
CHORUS.
All joy His loved ones bringing, When Jesus comes:
All praise thro' heaven ringing, When Jesus comes. All beauty bright and vernal,
When Je-sus comes; All glo-ry, grand, e-ter-nal, When Je-sus comes.

3 No more heart-pangs nor sadness,
When Jesus comes;
All peace and joy and gladness,
When Jesus comes. *Cho.*

4 All doubts and fears will vanish,
When Jesus comes:
All gloom His face will banish,
When Jesus comes. *Cho.*

5 He'll know the way was dreary,
When Jesus comes;
He'll know the feet grew weary,
When Jesus comes. *Cho.*

6 He'll know what griefs oppressed me,
When Jesus comes;
Oh, how His arms will rest me!
When Jesus comes. *Cho.*

No. 53. White as Snow.

"Come now, and let us reason together, saith the LORD: though your sins be as scarlet, they shall be as white as snow."—ISA. 1: 18.

Words by L. N. P. P. BLISS, by per.

1. What! "lay my sins on Je - sus?" God's well - be - lov - ed Son!
No! 'tis a truth most pre - cious, That God e'en *that* has done.
CHORUS.
Hal - le - lu - jah, Je - sus saves me, He makes me "white as snow."
Hal - le - lu - jah, Je - sus saves me, He makes me "white as snow."

2.

Yes, 'tis a truth most precious,
To all who do believe,
God laid our sins on Jesus,
Who did the load receive. *Cho.*

3.

What! "bring our guilt to Jesus?"
To wash away our stains;
The act is passed that freed us,
And nought to do remains. *Cho.*

No. 54. Just as I Am. L. M.

"Him that cometh to Me, I will in no wise cast out."—JOHN 6 : 37.

Miss CHARLOTTE ELLIOTT, 1834. WM. B. BRADBURY, by per.

1. Just as I am, without one plea, But that Thy blood was shed for me,
And that Thou bidd'st me come to Thee, O Lamb of God! I come, I come!

2 Just as I am, and waiting not
To rid my soul of one dark blot, [spot,
To Thee, whose blood can cleanse each
O Lamb of God! I come, I come!

3 Just as I am, though tossed about,
With many a conflict, many a doubt,
Fightings and fears within, without,
O Lamb of God! I come, I come!

4 Just as I am, poor, wretched, blind,
Sight, riches, healing of the mind,
Yea, all I need, in Thee to find,
O Lamb of God! I come, I come!

5 Just as I am; Thou wilt receive,
Wilt welcome, pardon, cleanse, relieve;
Because Thy promise I believe,
O Lamb of God! I come, I come!

No. 55. To-Day. 6s & 4s.

"To-day if ye will hear His voice."—PSA. 95: 7.

Rev. S. F. SMITH. DR. L. MASON, 1831.

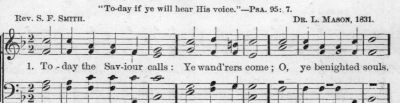

1. To-day the Saviour calls: Ye wand'rers come; O, ye benighted souls,

Why longer roam?

2 To-day the Saviour calls:
Oh, listen now:
Within these sacred walls
To Jesus bow.

3 To-day the Saviour calls:
For refuge fly;
The storm of justice falls,
And death is nigh.

4 The Spirit calls to-day:
Yield to His power;
Oh, grieve Him not away;
'Tis mercy's hour.

No. 56. The Great Physician.

"Is there no balm in Gilead; is there no physician there?"—JER. 8: 22.

Rev. WM. HUNTER, 1844. Arr. by Rev. J. H. STOCKTON.

p
1. The great Phy - si - cian now is near, The sym - pa - thiz - ing
Je - sus: He speaks the drooping heart to cheer, Oh, hear the voice of
CHORUS.
Je - sus. Sweetest note in ser - aph song, Sweetest name on
mortal tongue, Sweetest car-ol ev - er sung, Je - sus, blessed Je - sus.
pp

2 Your many sins are all forgiven,
Oh, hear the voice of Jesus;
Go on your way in peace to heaven,
And wear a crown with Jesus.

3 All glory to the dying Lamb!
I now believe in Jesus;
I love the blessed Saviour's name,
I love the name of Jesus.

4 The children too, both great and small,
Who love the name of Jesus,
May now accept the gracious call
To work and live for Jesus.

5 Come, brethren, help me sing His praise,
Oh, praise the name of Jesus;
Come, sisters, all your voices raise,
Oh, bless the name of Jesus.

6 His name dispels my guilt and fear,
No other name but Jesus;
Oh, how my soul delights to hear
The precious name of Jesus.

7 And when to that bright world above,
We rise to see our Jesus,
We'll sing around the throne of love
His name, the name of Jesus.

No. 57. Substitution.

"He was wounded for our transgressions."—ISAIAH 53: 5.

MRS. A. R. COUSIN. IRA D. SANKEY, by per.

1. O Christ, what burdens bowed Thy head! Our load was laid on Thee; Thou
2. Death and the curse were in our cup— O Christ, 'twas full for Thee! But
stood - est in the sinner's stead, Didst bear all ill for me. A
Thou hast drained the last dark drop—'Tis emp - ty now for me. That
Vic - tim led, Thy blood was shed; Now there's no load for me.
bit - ter cup—love drank it up; Now bless - ings' draught for me.

3.

Jehovah lifted up His rod—
O Christ, it fell on Thee!
Thou wast sore stricken of Thy God;
There's not one stroke for me.
Thy tears, Thy blood, beneath it flowed;
Thy bruising healeth me.

4.

The tempest's awful voice was heard—
O Christ, it broke on Thee!
Thy open bosom was my ward,
It braved the storm for me.
Thy form was scarred, Thy visage marred:
Now cloudless peace for me.

5.

Jehovah bade His sword awake—
O Christ, it woke 'gainst Thee!
Thy blood the flaming blade must slake;
Thy heart its sheath must be—
All for my sake, my peace to make;
Now sleeps that sword for me.

6.

For me, Lord Jesus, Thou hast died,
And I have died in Thee;
Thou'rt risen: my bands are all untied,
And now Thou liv'st in me.
When purified, made white, and tried,
Thy GLORY then for me!

No. 58. In the Presence of the King.

"In Thy presence is fulness of joy; at Thy right hand there are pleasures for evermore."—PSALM 16: 11.

Miss FLORENCE C. ARMSTRONG. 1864. English.

Moderato.
1. Oh, to be o-ver yon-der! In that land of won-der, Where the
2. Oh, to be o-ver yon-der! My yearning heart grows fonder Of
an-gel voi-ces min-gle, And the an-gel harpers ring; To be
look-ing to the east, to see the blessed day-star bring Some
p
cres.
free from pain and sor-row, And the anxious, dread to-mor-row, To
tid-ings of the wak-ing, The cloudless, pure day breaking; My
f
rit.
tempo.
rest in light and sunshine In the pre-sence of the King.
heart is yearning—yearning for the com-ing of the King.

3 Oh, to be over yonder!
Alas! I sigh and wonder
why clings my poor, weak, sinful heart to any earthly thing;
Each tie of earth must sever,
And pass away for ever;
But there's no more separation in the presence of the King.

4 Oh, when shall I be dwelling
Where angel voices, swelling
In triumphant hallelujahs, make the vaulted heavens ring?
Where the pearly gates are gleaming,
And the morning star is beaming?
Oh, when shall I be yonder in the presence of the King?

In the Presence of the King.—Concluded.

5 Oh, when shall I be yonder?
The longing groweth stronger
To join in all the praises the redeemed ones do sing
Within those heavenly places,
Where the angels vail their faces,
In awe and adoration in the presence of the King.

6 Oh I shall soon be yonder,
And lonely as I wander,
Yearning for the welcome summer—longing for the bird's fleet wing;
The midnight may be dreary,
And the heart be worn and weary,
But there's no more shadow yonder, in the presence of the King.

No. 59. I am Coming to the Cross.

"Him that cometh to Me I will in no wise cast out."—John 6: 37.

Rev. Wm. McDonald. Wm. G. Fischer, by per.

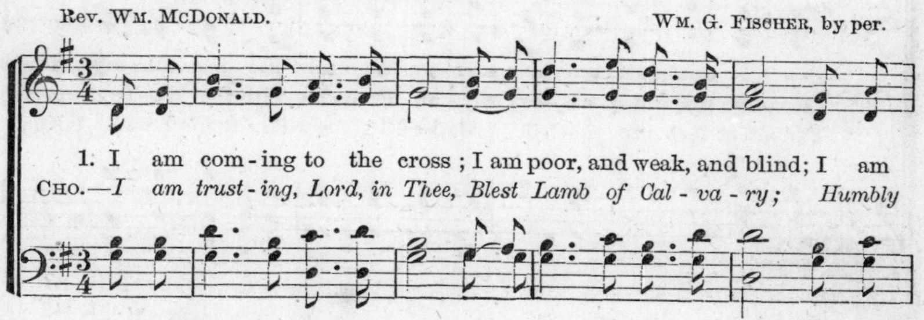
1. I am com - ing to the cross; I am poor, and weak, and blind; I am
Cho.—I am trust - ing, Lord, in Thee, Blest Lamb of Cal - va - ry; Humbly

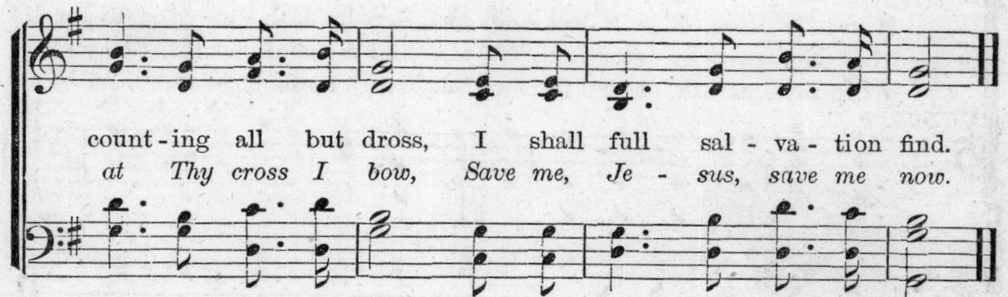
count - ing all but dross, I shall full sal - va - tion find.
at Thy cross I bow, Save me, Je - sus, save me now.

2 Long my heart has sighed for Thee,
Long has evil reigned within;
Jesus sweetly speaks to me,—
"I will cleanse you from all sin. *Cho.*

3 Here I give my all to Thee,
Friends, and time, and earthly store;
Soul and body Thine to be,—
Wholly Thine for evermore. *Cho.*

4 In thy promises I trust,
Now I feel the blood applied:
I am prostrate in the dust,
I with Christ am crucified. *Cho.*

5 Jesus comes! He fills my soul!
Perfected in Him I am;
I am every whit made whole:
Glory, glory to the Lamb. *Cho.*

No. 60. All the Way My Saviour Leads Me.

"The Lord alone did lead him."—DEUT. 32: 12.

FANNY J. CROSBY. Rev. R. LOWRY, by per.

1. All the way my Saviour leads me; What have I to ask be-side?
2. All the way my Saviour leads me; Cheers each winding path I tread;
3. All the way my Saviour leads me; Oh, the fullness of His love!
Can I doubt His ten-der mer-cy, Who thro' life has been my guide?
Gives me grace for ev-ery tri-al, Feeds me with the liv-ing bread;
Per-fect rest to me is promised In my Fa-ther's house a-bove;
Heaven'ly peace, di-vin-est com-fort, Here by faith in Him to dwell!
Tho' my wea-ry steps may fal-ter, And my soul a-thirst may be,
When my spir-it, cloth'd immor-tal, Wings its flight to realms of day,
For I know what-e'er be-fall me, Je-sus do-eth all things
Gushing from the Rock be-fore me, Lo! a spring of joy I
This my song through endless a-ges— Je-sus led me all the

All the Way.—Concluded.

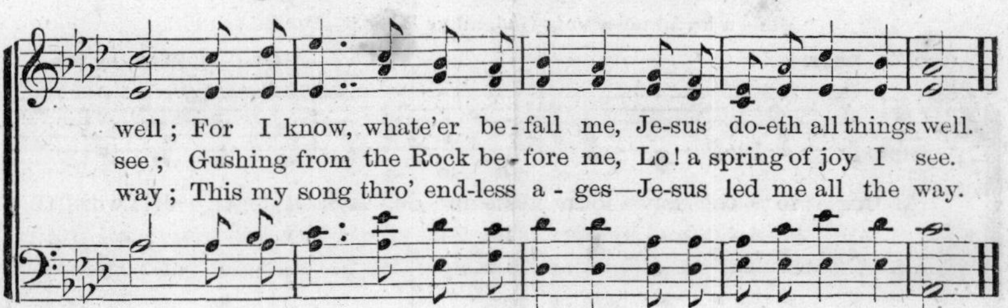
well; For I know, whate'er be-fall me, Je-sus do-eth all things well.
see; Gushing from the Rock be-fore me, Lo! a spring of joy I see.
way; This my song thro' end-less a-ges—Je-sus led me all the way.

No. 61. Go Bury thy Sorrow.

"They shall obtain joy and gladness, and sorrow and sighing shall flee away."—Isaiah 35: 10.

Anon. P. P. Bliss, by per,

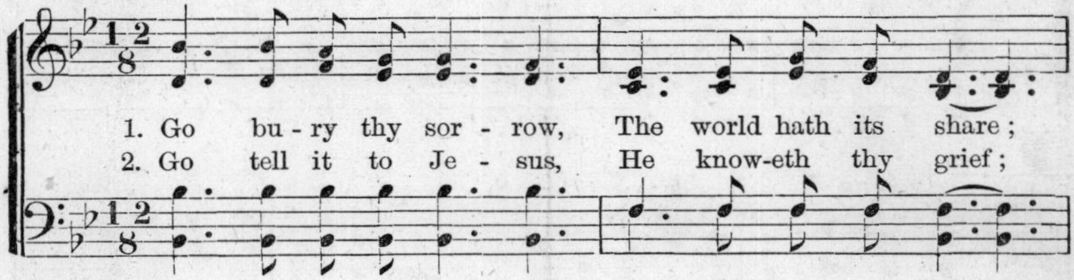

1. Go bu-ry thy sor-row, The world hath its share;
2. Go tell it to Je-sus, He know-eth thy grief;

Go bu-ry it deep-ly, Go hide it with care, Go think of it calm-ly,
Go tell it to Je-sus, He'll send thee relief, Go gather the sun-shine

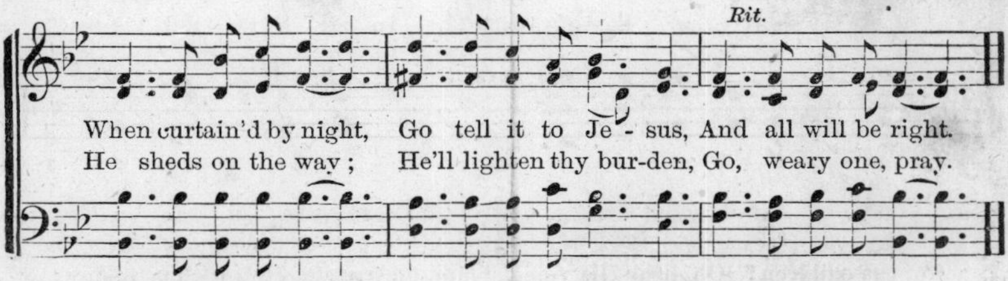

Rit.

When curtain'd by night, Go tell it to Je-sus, And all will be right.
He sheds on the way; He'll lighten thy bur-den, Go, weary one, pray.

3 Hearts growing a-weary
With heavier woe
Now droop 'mid the darkness—
Go comfort them, go!

Go bury thy sorrows,
Let others be blest;
Go give them the sunshine,
Tell Jesus the rest.

No. 62. Come to the Saviour.

"Make a joyful noise unto God, all ye lands."—PSALM. 66: 1.

GEO. F. ROOT. GEO. F. ROOT, by per.

Earnestly.
1. Come to the Sav - iour, make no de - lay; Here in His word He's shown us the way; Here in our midst He's standing to-day, Tenderly saying, "Come!"
CHORUS.
Joy - ful, joyful will the meeting be, When from sin our hearts are pure and free;
And we shall gather, Saviour, with Thee, In our e - ter - nal home.

2.

"Suffer the children!" Oh, hear His voice,
Let ev'ry heart leap forth and rejoice,
And let us freely make Him our choice;
Do not delay, but come. *Cho.*

3.

Think once again, He's with us to-day;
Heed now His blest commands, and obey;
Hear now His accents tenderly say,
"Will you, my children, come?" *Cho.*

No. 63. I Hear Thy Welcome Voice.

"Come unto Me, all ye that labor and are heavy-laden, and I will give you rest."—MATT. 11: 28.

Rev. L. HARTSOUGH. From "Hallowed Songs," by per.

1. I hear Thy welcome voice That calls me, Lord, to Thee For
2. Tho' com - ing weak and vile, Thou dost my strength assure; Thou
cleans - ing in Thy pre - cious blood That flowed on Cal - va - ry.
dost my vile-ness ful - ly cleanse, Till spot - less all and pure.
CHORUS.
I am com - ing Lord! Com - ing now to Thee!
Wash me, cleanse me, in the blood That flowed on Cal - va - ry.

3 'Tis Jesus calls me on
To perfect faith and love,
To perfect hope, and peace, and trust,
For earth and heaven above.

4 'Tis Jesus who confirms
The blessed work within,
By adding grace to welcomed grace,
Where reigned the power of sin.

5 And He the witness gives
To loyal hearts and free,
That every promise is fulfilled,
If faith but brings the plea.

6 All hail, atoning blood!
All hail, redeeming grace!
All hail, the Gift of Christ, our Lord,
Our Strength and Righteousness!

No. 64. A Sinner Forgiven.

"He said unto her, thy sins are forgiven."—LUKE 7: 48.

ENGLISH. Arranged.

1. To the hall of the feast came the sin-ful and fair; She heard in the
2. The frown and the murmur went round through them all, That one so un-
cit-y that Je-sus was there; Un-heed-ing the splendor that
hallowed should tread in that hall; And some said the poor would be
blazed on the board, She si-lent-ly knelt at the feet of the
ob-jects more meet, As the wealth of her per-fume she shower'd on His
Lord, She si-lent-ly knelt at the feet of the Lord.
feet, As the wealth of her per-fume she shower'd on His feet.

3 She heard but the Saviour; she spoke but with sighs;
She dare not look up to the heaven of His eyes;
And the hot tears gush'd forth at each heave of her breast,
As her lips to His sandals were throbbingly pressed.

4 In the sky, after tempest, as shineth the bow,—
In the glance of the sunbeam, as melteth the snow
He looked on that lost one: "her sins were forgiven,"
And the sinner went forth in the beauty of heaven.

No. 65. Let the Lower Lights be Burning.

"Let your light so shine before men, that they may see your good works, and glorify your Father which is in heaven."—MATT. 5: 16.

P. P. BLISS. P. P. BLISS, by per.

1. Bright-ly beams our Fa-ther's mer-cy From His light-house ev - er -
more, But to us He gives the keeping Of the lights along the shore.
CHORUS.
Let the low - er lights be burning! Send a gleam across the wave! Some poor
faint - ing, struggling sea-man You may res-cue, you may save.

2 Dark the night of sin has settled,
Loud the angry billows roar;
Eager eyes are watching, longing,
For the lights along the shore.—*Cho.*

3 Trim your feeble lamp, my brother:
Some poor sailor tempest-tost,
Trying now to make the harbor,
In the darkness *may be lost.*—*Cho.*

No. 66. Wishing, Hoping, Knowing.

"My beloved is mine, and I am His."—SONGS OF SOLOMON 2: 16.

P. P. BLISS. P. P. BLISS, by per.

1. A long time I wandered in darkness and sin, And wondered if ev - er the
2. I heard the glad gos-pel of "good will to men;" I read "who-so-ev - er" a -
light would shine in; I heard Christian friends tell of rapture di - vine, And
gain and a - gain; I said to my soul, "Can that promise be thine?" And
CHORUS.
wish'd, how I wish'd, that their Saviour were mine. I wish'd He were mine, yes, I
then be - gan hop-ing that Je - sus was mine. I hoped He was mine, yes, I
wish'd He were mine; I wished, how I wished, that their Saviour were mine.
hoped He was mine; I then be - gan hop-ing that Je - sus was mine.

3 Oh, mercy surprising, He saves even me!
"Thy portion forever," He says, "will I be,"
On His word I'm resting—assurance divine—
I'm "hoping" no longer—I know He is mine!

Chorus.—I know He is mine, yes, I know He is mine;
I'm "hoping" no longer—I know He is mine!

No. 67. Varina. C. M. D.

"Thine eyes shall behold the land that is very far off."—Isa. 33 : 17.

Rev. I. Watts. Geo. F. Root, by per.

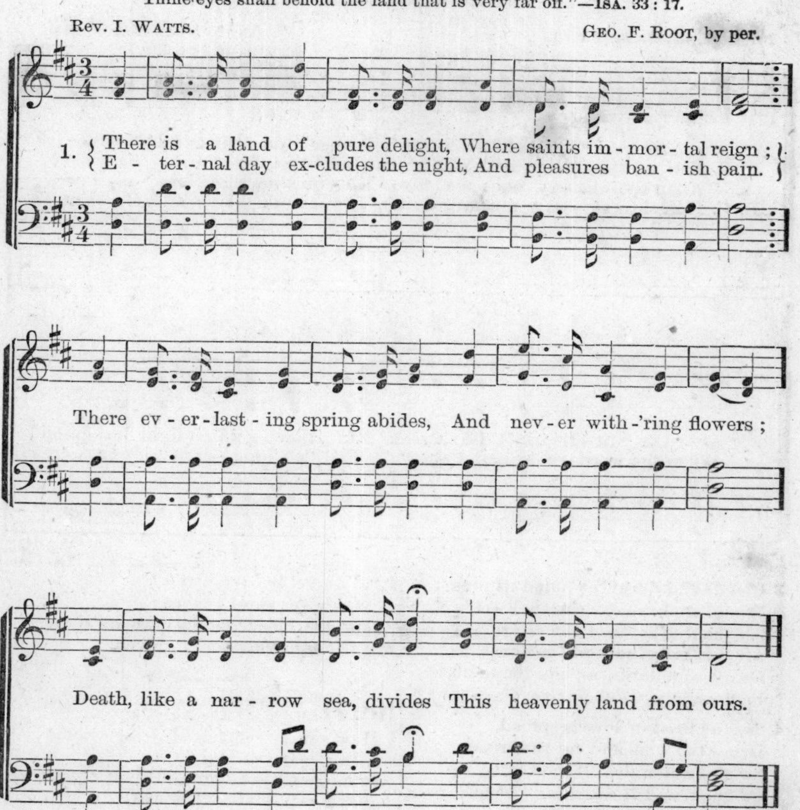
1. { There is a land of pure delight, Where saints im - mor - tal reign ;
E - ter - nal day ex-cludes the night, And pleasures ban - ish pain. }
There ev - er - last - ing spring abides, And nev - er with -'ring flowers ;
Death, like a nar - row sea, divides This heavenly land from ours.

2 Sweet fields beyond the swelling flood
Stand dressed in living green ;
So to the Jews old Canaan stood,
While Jordan rolled between.
Could we but climb where Moses stood,
And view the landscape o'er,
Not Jordan's stream, nor death's cold flood,
Should fright us from the shore.

No. 68. Rathbun. 8s & 7s. Key C.

1 In the cross of Christ I glory,
Towering o'er the wrecks of time ;
All the light of sacred story,
Gathers round its head sublime.

2 When the woes of life o'ertake me,
Hopes deceive and fears annoy,
Never shall the cross forsake me ;
Lo ! it glows with peace and joy.

3 When the sun of bliss is beaming
Light and love upon my way,
From the cross the radiance streaming,
Adds new luster to the day.

4 Bain and blessing, pain and pleasure,
By the cross are sanctified ;
Peace is there, that knows no measure,
Joys that through all time abide.

No. 69. Till He Come.

"For yet a little while and He that shall come will come, and will not tarry."—HEB. 10: 37.

Rev. ED. H. BICKERSTETH. Dr. LOWELL MASON, 1840.

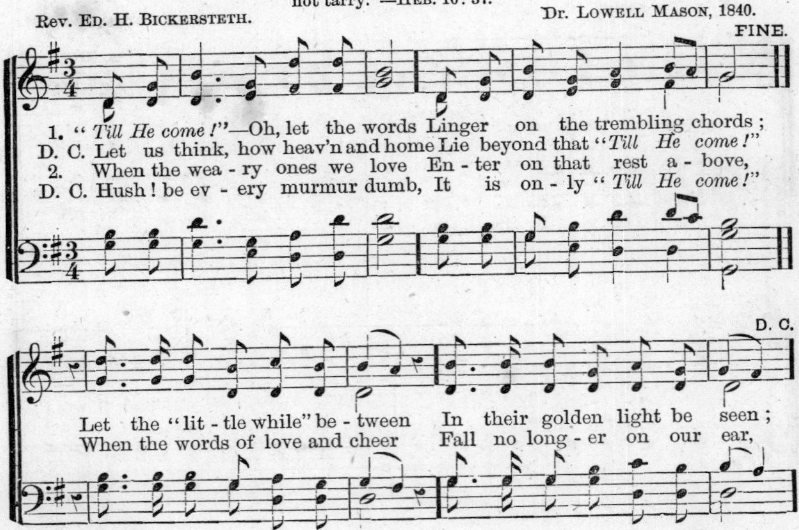
FINE.
1. "*Till He come!*"—Oh, let the words Linger on the trembling chords;
D. C. Let us think, how heav'n and home Lie beyond that "*Till He come!*"
2. When the wea - ry ones we love En - ter on that rest a - bove,
D. C. Hush! be ev - ery murmur dumb, It is on - ly "*Till He come!*"
D. C.
Let the "lit - tle while" be - tween In their golden light be seen;
When the words of love and cheer Fall no long - er on our ear,

3 Clouds and darkness round us press;
Would we have one sorrow less?
All the sharpness of the cross,
All that tells the world is loss,
Death, and darkness, and the tomb,
Pain us only "*Till He come!*"

4 See the feast of love is spread,
Drink the wine and eat the bread;
Sweet memorials, till the Lord
Call us round His heavenly board,
Some from earth, from glory some,
Severed only "*Till He come!*"

No. 70.

DENNIS. S. M.
Key F.

1 How solemn are the words,
And yet to faith how plain,
Which Jesus uttered while on earth—
"*Ye must be born again!*"

2 "*Ye must be born again!*"
For so hath God decreed;
No reformation will suffice—
'Tis *life* poor sinners need.

3 "*Ye must be born again!*"
And life *in Christ* must have;
In vain the soul may elsewhere go—
s He *alone* can save.

4 "*Ye must be born again!*"
Or never enter heaven;
'Tis only blood-washed ones are there—
The ransomed and forgiven.

ANON.

No. 71.

ORTONVILLE. C. M.
Key B♭.

1 How sweet the name of Jesus sounds
In a believer's ear;
It soothes His sorrows, heals His wounds,
And drives away His fear.

2 It makes the wounded spirit whole,
And calms the troubled breast;
'Tis manna to the hungry soul,
And to the weary, rest.

3 Dear Name, the Rock on which I build,
My shield and hiding-place;
My never-failing treasure, filled
With boundless stores of grace.

4 Jesus my Shepherd, Saviour, Friend,
My Prophet, Priest, and King,
My Lord, my Life, My Way, my End,
Accept the praise I bring.

5 I would Thy boundless love proclaim
With every fleeting breath;
So shall the music of Thy name
Refresh my soul in death.

Rev. JOHN NEWTON.

No. 72. The Precious Name.

"And blessed be His glorious name for ever."—Psa. 72 : 19.

Mrs. Lydia Baxter. W. H. Doane, by per.

1. Take the name of Je - sus with you, Child of sor-row and of woe—
2. Take the name of Je - sus ev - er, As a shield from every snare;
It will joy and comfort give you, Take it then where'er you go.
If temptations 'round you gath - er, Breathe that ho - ly name in pray'r.
CHORUS.
Precious name, O how sweet! Hope of earth and joy of
Precious name, O how sweet!
heaven, Precious name, O how sweet—Hope of earth and joy of heav'n.
Precious name, O how sweet, how sweet,

3 Oh! the precious name of Jesus;
How it thrills our souls with joy,
When His loving arms receive us,
And His songs our tongues employ! *Cho.*

4 At the name of Jesus bowing,
Falling prostrate at His feet,
King of kings in heav'n we'll crown Him,
When our journey is complete. *Cho.*

No. 73. "It Passeth Knowledge."

"The love of Christ, which passeth knowledge."—Eph. 3: 19.

Mary Shekleton. Ira D. Sankey, by per.

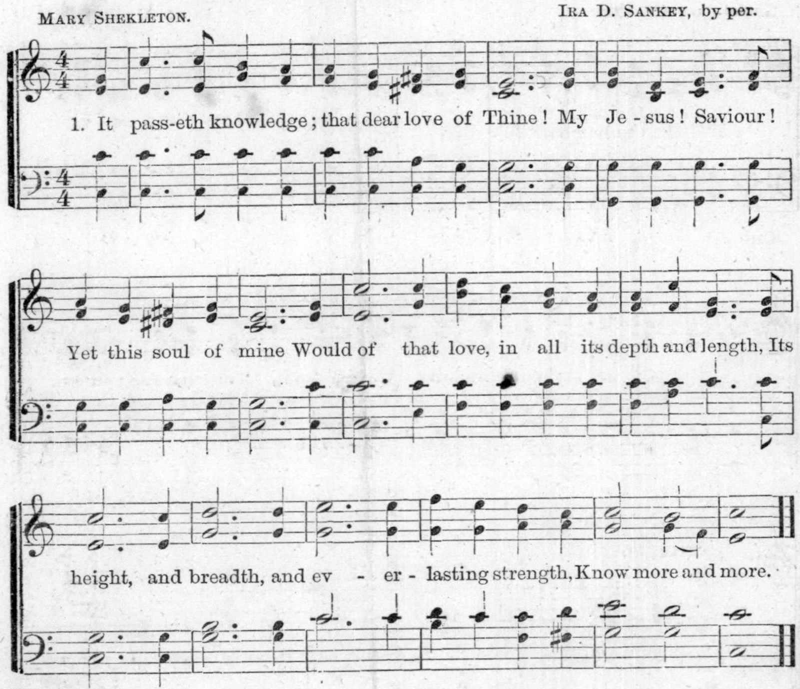
1. It pass-eth knowledge; that dear love of Thine! My Je - sus! Saviour!
Yet this soul of mine Would of that love, in all its depth and length, Its
height, and breadth, and ev - er - lasting strength, Know more and more.

2,

It passeth *telling!* that dear love of Thine,
My Jesus! Saviour! Yet these lips of mine
Would fain proclaim to sinners far and near
A love which can remove all guilty fear,
And love beget.

3.

It passeth *praises!* that dear love of Thine,
My Jesus! Saviour! Yet this heart of mine
Would sing a love so rich, so full, so free,
Which brought an undone sinner, such as me,
Right home to God.

4.

But ah! I cannot tell, or sing, or know,
The fulness of that love, whilst here below;
Yet my poor vessel I may freely bring,
O Thou who art of love the living spring,
My vessel fill.

5.

I *am* an empty vessel! scarce one thought
Or look of love to Thee I've ever brought;
Yet, I *may* come, and come again to Thee
With this—the contrite sinner's truthful plea—
"Thou lovest me!"

6.

Oh! *fill* me, Jesus! Saviour! with Thy love!
May woes but drive me to the fount above:
Thither may I in childlike faith draw nigh,
And never to another fountain fly
But unto Thee!

7.

And when, my Jesus! Thy dear face I see,
When at Thy lofty throne I bend the knee,
Then of Thy love—in all its breadth and length,
Its height, and depth, and everlasting strength—
My soul shall sing.

No. 74. Oh, to be Nothing.

"Neither is he that planteth anything, neither he that watereth."—1 Cor. 3: 7.

Georgiana M. Taylor, 1869. R. Geo. Halls. Arr. by P. P. Bliss.

Very slow.
1. Oh, to be nothing, noth - ing, On - ly to lie at His feet,
Cho. Oh, to be nothing, noth - ing, On - ly to lie at His feet,
FINE.
A broken and emptied ves - sel, For the Mas - ter's use made meet.
A broken and emptied ves - sel, For the Mas - ter's use made meet.
Emptied that He might fill me As forth to His service I go;
D. C. CHORUS.
Broken, that so un - hin - dered, His life through me might flow.

2 Oh, to be nothing, nothing,
Only as led by His hand;
A messenger at His gateway,
Only waiting for His command,
Only an instrument ready
His praises to sound at His will,
Willing, should He not require me,
In silence to wait on Him still. *Cho.*

3 Oh, to be nothing, nothing,
Painful the humbling may be,
Yet low in the dust I'd lay me
That the world might my Saviour see.
Rather be nothing, nothing,
To Him let their voices be raised,
He is the Fountain of blessing,
He only is meet to be praised. *Cho.*

Almost Persuaded.

No. 75.

"Almost Thou persuadest me to be a Christian."—Acts 26: 28.

P. P. Bliss. P. P. Bliss, by per.

1. "Al - most per - suad - ed" Now to be - lieve;
2. "Al - most per - suad - ed," Come, come to - day;
"Al - most per - suad - ed" Christ to re - ceive;
"Al - most per - suad - ed," Turn not a - way;
Seems now some soul to say, "Go, Spir - it, go Thy way,
Je - sus in - vites you here, An - gels are lingering near,
Some more con - ven - ient day On Thee I'll call."
Prayers rise from hearts so dear: O wanderer, come.

3 "Almost persuaded," harvest is past!
"Almost persuaded," doom comes at last!
"Almost" can not avail;
"Almost" is but to fail!
Sad, sad, that bitter wail—
"Almost—*but lost!*"

No. 76. Fully Persuaded.

"Believe on the Lord Jesus Christ and thou shalt be saved."—Acts 16: 31.

Rev. J. B. Atchinson. Wm. F. Sherwin, by per.

1. Ful - ly per - suad - ed, Lord, I be - lieve!
2. Ful - ly per - suad - ed— Lord, hear my cry!

Ful - ly per - suad - ed, Thy Spir - it give;
Ful - ly per - suad - ed— pass me not by;

I will o - bey Thy call; Low at Thy feet I fall;
Just as I am I come, I will no lon - ger roam,

rit.

Now I sur - ren - der all, Christ to re - ceive.
O make my heart Thy home; Save, or I die!

3.

Fully persuaded, no more opprest,
Fully persuaded, now I am blest:
Jesus is now my Guide,
I will in Christ abide;
My soul is satisfied
In Him to rest!

4.

Fully persuaded, Jesus is mine;
Fully persuaded, Lord, I am Thine!
O make my love to Thee
Like Thine own love to me,
So rich, so full and free,
Saviour divine!

No. 77. Sweet Hour of Prayer.

"Evening, and morning, and at noon will I pray."—PSALM 4 : 17.

Rev. W. W. WALFORD, 1846. WM. B. BRADBURY, 1859.

Slow.
1. Sweet hour of prayer! sweet hour of prayer! That calls me from a world of care, And bids me at my Fa - ther's throne Make all my wants and wish - es known: In sea - sons of dis - tress and grief, My soul has oft - en found re - lief;
D. C. And oft es - caped the tempter's snare, By thy re - turn, sweet hour of prayer, And oft es - caped the tempter's snare, By thy re - turn, sweet hour of prayer!
FINE.
D. C.

2.

Sweet hour of prayer! sweet hour of prayer!
Thy wings shall my petition bear
To Him whose truth and faithfulness
Engage the waiting soul to bless.
And since He bids me seek His face,
Believe His word, and trust His grace,
‖: I'll cast on Him my every care
And wait for thee, sweet hour of prayer! :‖

3.

Sweet hour of prayer! sweet hour of prayer!
May I thy consolation share,
Till, from Mount Pisgah's lofty height,
I view my home and take my flight:
This robe of flesh I'll drop, and rise
To seize the everlasting prize;
‖: And shout, while passing through the air,
Farewell, farewell, sweet hour of prayer! :‖

No. 78. No Other Name.

"Neither is there salvation in any other."—Acts 4: 12.

P. P. Bliss. P. P. Bliss, by per.

1. One of - fer of sal - va - tion, To all the world make known;
The on - ly sure foun-da - tion Is Christ the Cor - ner - Stone.
CHORUS.
No oth - er name is giv - en, No oth - er way is known, 'Tis
Je - sus Christ the First and Last, He saves, and He a - lone.

2 One only door of heaven
Stands open wide to-day,
One sacrifice is given,
'Tis Christ, the living way. *Cho.*

3 My only song and story
Is—Jesus died for me;
My only hope of glory,
The Cross of Calvary. *Cho.*

No. 79. What Shall the Harvest Be?

"Whatsoever a man soweth, that shall he also reap."—GAL. 6: 7.

ANON. P. P. BLISS, by per.

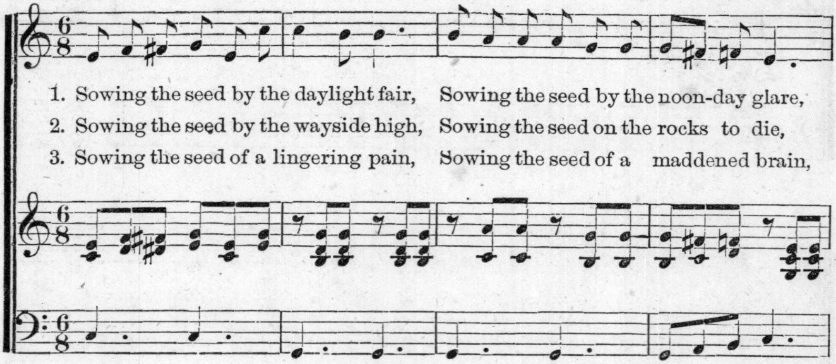

1. Sowing the seed by the daylight fair, Sowing the seed by the noon-day glare,
2. Sowing the seed by the wayside high, Sowing the seed on the rocks to die,
3. Sowing the seed of a lingering pain, Sowing the seed of a maddened brain,

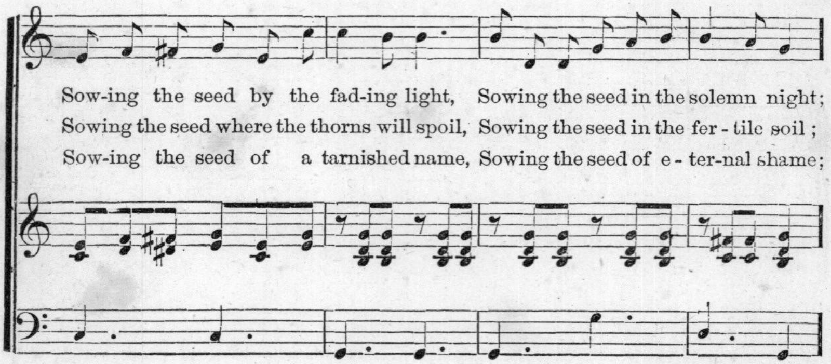

Sow-ing the seed by the fad-ing light, Sowing the seed in the solemn night;
Sowing the seed where the thorns will spoil, Sowing the seed in the fer-tile soil;
Sow-ing the seed of a tarnished name, Sowing the seed of e-ter-nal shame;

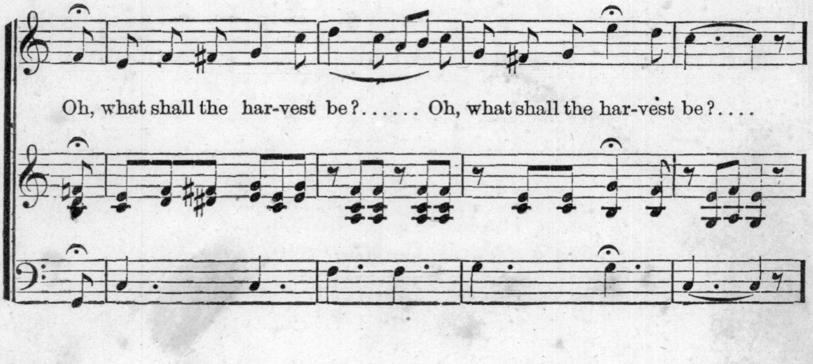

Oh, what shall the har-vest be?...... Oh, what shall the har-vest be?....

What Shall the Harvest Be.—Concluded.

CHORUS.
Sown......... in the dark - - - - ness or sown........ in the
Sown in the darkness or sown in the light, Sown in the darkness or
light,......... Sown......... in our weak - - - ness or
sown in the light, Sown in our weakness or sown in our might,
sown.......... in our might,....... Gath - ered in time or e-
Sown in our weakness or sown in our might, Gath - ered in time or e-
ter - ni - ty, Sure, ah, sure will the har - - vest be.....
ter - ni - ty, Sure, ah, sure will the har - vest, harvest be.

4 Sowing the seed with an aching heart
Sowing the seed while the tear-drops start
Sowing in hope till the reapers come
Gladly to gather the harvest home:
Oh, what shall the harvest be?
Oh, what shall the harvest be?

No. 80. There is Life for a Look.

"Look unto Me and be ye saved, all the ends of the earth."—ISAIAH. 14: 22.

AMELIA M. HULL. Rev. E. G. TAYLOR, by per.

1. There is life for a look at the Cru - ci - fied One, There is
life at this moment for thee; Then look, sinner, look unto Him and be saved, Unto
Him who was nailed to the tree.
REFRAIN.
Look! look! look and live! There is
life for a look at the Cru-ci - fied One, There is life at this moment for thee.

2 Oh, why was He there as the Bearer of sin,
If on Jesus thy guilt was not laid?
Oh why from His side flowed the sin-cleansing blood,
If His dying thy debt has not paid?

3 It is not thy tears of repentance and prayers,
But the *Blood*, that atones for the soul;
On Him, then, who shed it, thou mayest at once
Thy weight of iniquities roll.

4 Then doubt not thy welcome, since God has declared
There remaineth no more to be done;
That once in the end of the world He appeared,
And completed the work He begun.

5 Then take with rejoicing from Jesus at once
The life everlasting He gives;
And know with assurance thou never canst die
Since Jesus thy righteousness, lives.

No. 81. Yet There is Room.

"Yet there is room."—LUKE 14: 22.

Rev. H. BONAR, 1873. IRA D. SANKEY, by per.

Slow, with expression.

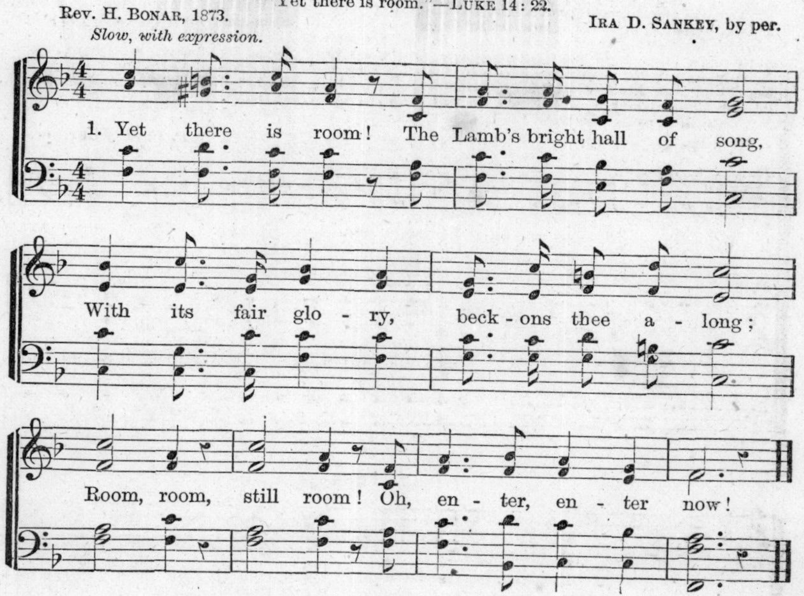
1. Yet there is room! The Lamb's bright hall of song,
With its fair glo - ry, beck - ons thee a - long;
Room, room, still room! Oh, en - ter, en - ter now!

2 Day is declining, and the sun is low;
The shadows lengthen, light makes haste to go:
Room, room, still room! oh, enter, enter now!

3 The bridal hall is filling for the feast:
Pass in, pass in, and be the Bridegroom's guest:
Room, room, still room! oh, enter, enter now!

4 It fills, it fills, that hall of jubilee!
Make haste, make haste; 'tis not too full for thee:
Room, room, still room! oh, enter, enter now!

5 Yet there is room! Still open stands the gate,
The gate of love; it is not yet too late:
Room, room, still room! oh, enter, enter now;

6 Pass in, pass in! That banquet is for thee;
That cup of everlasting love is free:
Room, room, still room! oh, enter, enter now!

7 All heaven is there, all joy! Go in, go in;
The angels beckon thee the prize to win:
Room, room, still room! oh, enter, enter now!

8 Louder and sweeter sounds the loving call;
Come lingerer, come; enter that festal hall:
Room, room, still room! oh, enter, enter now!

9 Ere night that gate may close, and seal thy doom:
Then the last, low, long cry;—"No room, no room!"
No room, no room:—oh, woful cry, "No room!"

Words written for Messrs. M. & S.

No. 82. Only an Armour-Bearer.

"Now it came to pass upon a day, that Jonathan the son of Saul said unto the young man that bare his armour, Come, and let us go over to the Philistines' garrison that *is* on the other side; it may be that the LORD will work for us: for *there is* no restraint to the LORD to save by many or by few. And his armour-bearer said unto him, Do all that *is* in thine heart: turn thee; behold, I *am* with thee according to thine heart. And Jonathan climbed up upon his hands and upon his feet, and his armour-bearer after him: and they fell before Jonathan; and his armour-bearer slew after him. So the LORD saved Israel that day: and the battle passed over unto Beth-aven."—1 SAM. 14: 1, 6, 7, 13, 23.

P. P. BLISS. P. P. BLISS, by per.

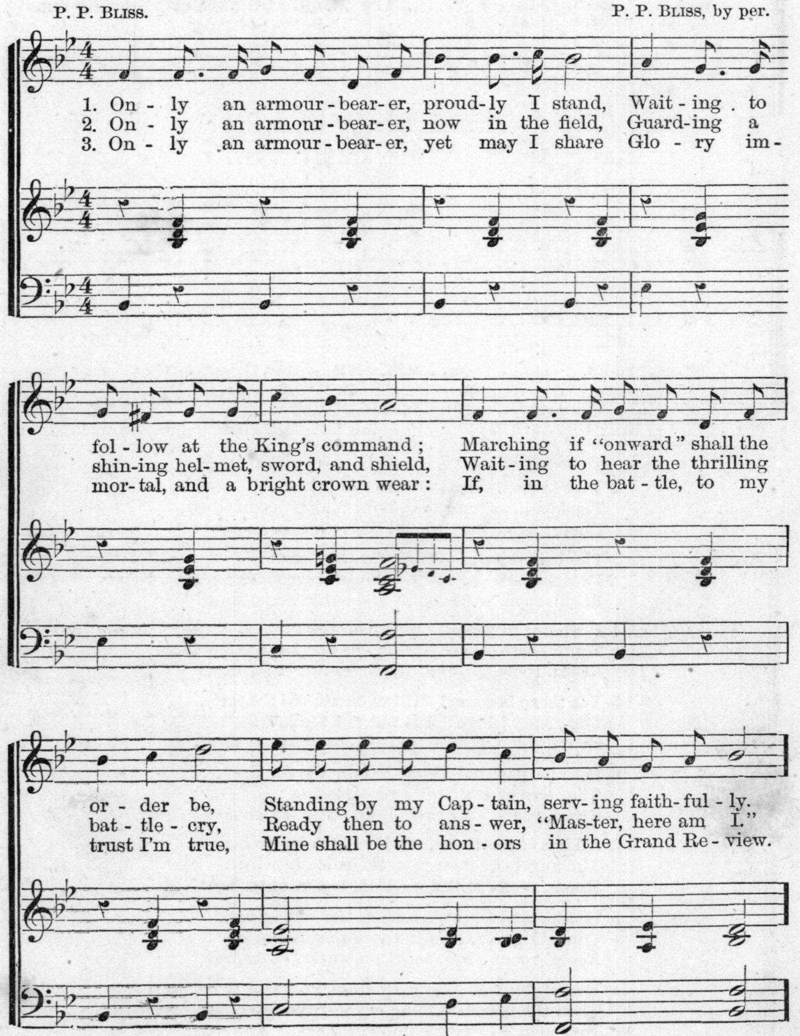
1. On - ly an armour - bear - er, proud - ly I stand, Wait - ing to
2. On - ly an armour - bear - er, now in the field, Guard - ing a
3. On - ly an armour - bear - er, yet may I share Glo - ry im -
fol - low at the King's command; Marching if "onward" shall the
shin - ing hel - met, sword, and shield, Wait - ing to hear the thrilling
mor - tal, and a bright crown wear: If, in the bat - tle, to my
or - der be, Standing by my Cap - tain, serv - ing faith - ful - ly.
bat - tle - cry, Ready then to an - swer, "Mas - ter, here am I."
trust I'm true, Mine shall be the hon - ors in the Grand Re - view.

Only an Armour-Bearer.—Concluded.

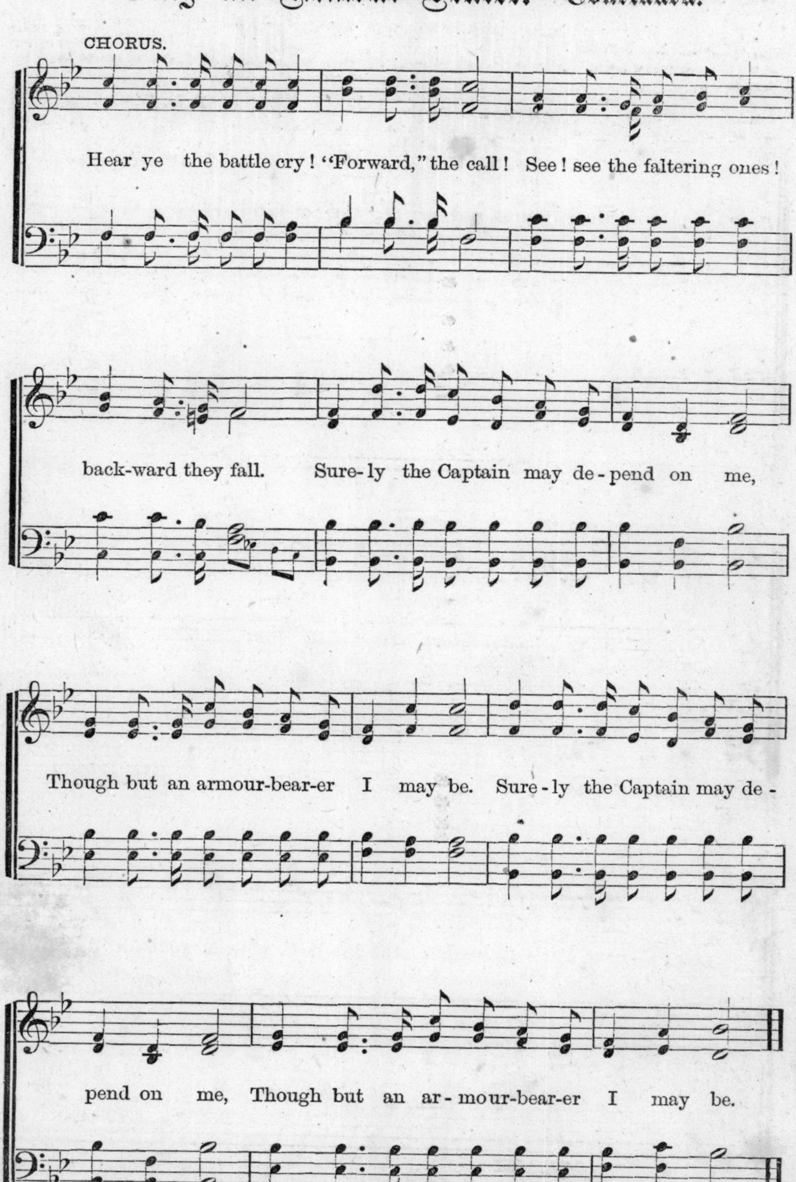
CHORUS.
Hear ye the battle cry! "Forward," the call! See! see the faltering ones!
back-ward they fall. Sure-ly the Captain may de-pend on me,
Though but an armour-bear-er I may be. Sure-ly the Captain may de-
pend on me, Though but an ar-mour-bear-er I may be.

No. 83. Pull for the Shore.

"Therefore, if any man be in Christ, he is a new creature; old things are passed away, behold, all things are become NEW."—2 COR. 5: 17.

"Therefore, my beloved, * * * work out your own salvation with fear and trembling."—PHIL. 2: 12.

P. P. BLISS. P. P. BLISS, by per.

1. Light in the darkness, sail - or, day is at hand! See o'er the foaming
bil - lows fair Ha - ven's land, Drear was the voy - age, sail - or,
now al - most o'er, Safe within the life-boat, sail - or, pull for the shore.

Pull for the Shore.—Concluded.

CHORUS.
Pull for the shore, sail - or, pull for the shore!
Heed not the roll - ing waves, but bend to the oar;
Safe in the life - boat, sail - or, cling to self no more!
Leave the poor old stranded wreck, and pull for the shore.

2 Trust in the life-boat, sailor, all else will fail,
Stronger the surges dash and fiercer the gale,
Heed not the stormy winds, though loudly they roar;
Watch the "bright and morning star," and pull for the shore.
Pull for the shore, &c.

3 Bright gleams the morning, sailor, up lift the eye;
Clouds and darkness disappearing, glory is nigh!
Safe in the life-boat, sailor, sing evermore;
"Glory, glory, hallelujah!" pull for the shore.
Pull for the shore, &c.

No. 84. Sun of My Soul.

"The Lord God is a sun."—Psa. 74: 11.

J. Keble, 1827. German. Arr. by W, H. Monk.

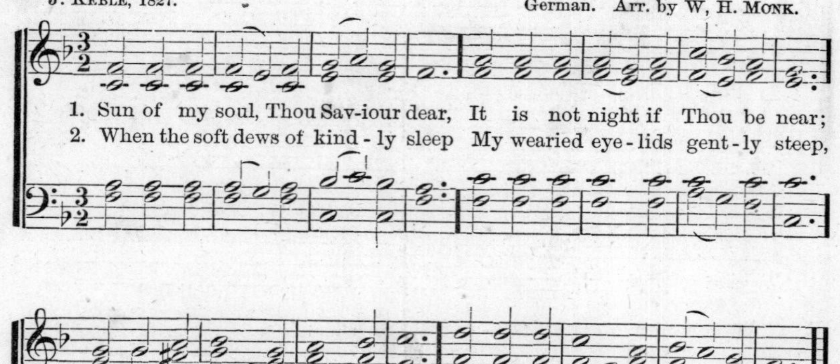
1. Sun of my soul, Thou Sav-iour dear, It is not night if Thou be near;
2. When the soft dews of kind - ly sleep My wearied eye - lids gent - ly steep,

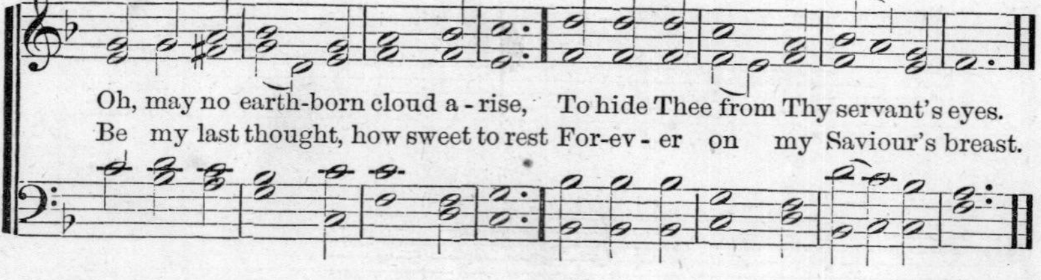
Oh, may no earth-born cloud a - rise, To hide Thee from Thy servant's eyes.
Be my last thought, how sweet to rest For-ev - er on my Saviour's breast.

3 Abide with me from morn till eve,
For without Thee I cannot live;
Abide with me when night is nigh,
For without Thee I dare not die.

4 If some poor wandering child of Thine
Have spurned to-day the voice divine—
Now, Lord, the gracious work begin;
Let him no more lie down in sin.

5 Watch by the sick: enrich the poor
With blessings from Thy boundless store;
Be every mourner's sleep to-night,
Like infant's slumbers, pure and light.

6 Come near and bless us when we wake,
Ere through the world our way we take,
Till in the ocean of Thy love
We lose ourselves in heaven above.

No. 85. Jesus, Lover of My Soul.

"The Lord will be a refuge in times of trouble."—Psalm 9: 9.

Rev. Ch. Wesley, 1740. Simeon B. Marsh, 1834.

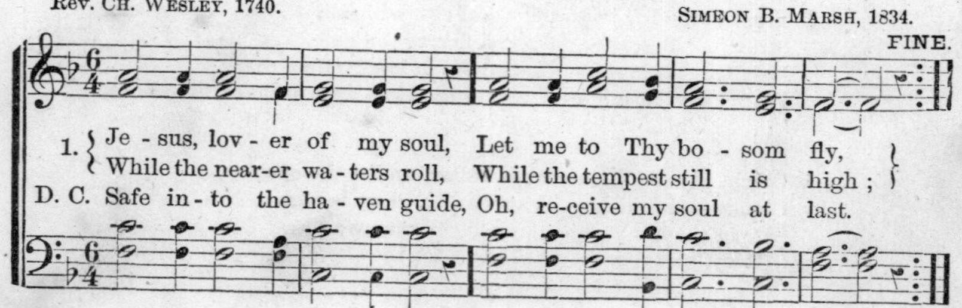
FINE.
1. { Je - sus, lov - er of my soul, Let me to Thy bo - som fly,
While the near-er wa - ters roll, While the tempest still is high; }
D. C. Safe in - to the ha - ven guide, Oh, re-ceive my soul at last.

Jesus, Lover of My Soul.—Concluded.

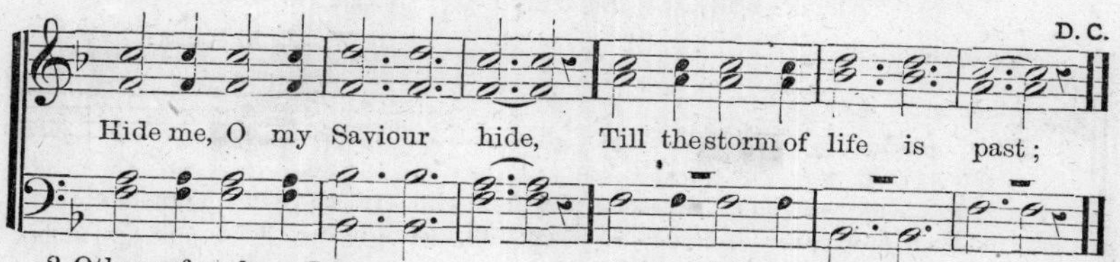
D. C.
Hide me, O my Saviour hide, Till the storm of life is past;

2 Other refuge have I none,
Hangs my helpless soul on Thee:
Leave, oh, leave me not alone,
Still support and comfort me.
All my trust on Thee is stayed
All my help from Thee I bring;
Cover my defenceless head
With the shadow of Thy wing.

3 Thou, O Christ, art all I want;
More than all in Thee I find:
Raise the fallen, cheer the faint,
Heal the sick, and lead the blind.
Just and holy is Thy Name,
I am all unrighteousness:
Vile, and full of sin I am,
Thou art full of truth and grace.

4 Plenteous grace with Thee is found—
Grace to cover all my sin:
Let the healing streams abound;
Make me, keep me, pure within.
Thou of life the Fountain art,
Freely let me take of Thee;
Spring Thou up within my heart,
Rise to all eternity.

No. 86. Rock of Ages.

"The Lord is my defence, and my God is the Rock of my refuge."—PSA. 94: 22.

REV. A. M. TOPLADY, 1776. DR. THOS. HASTINGS, 1830.

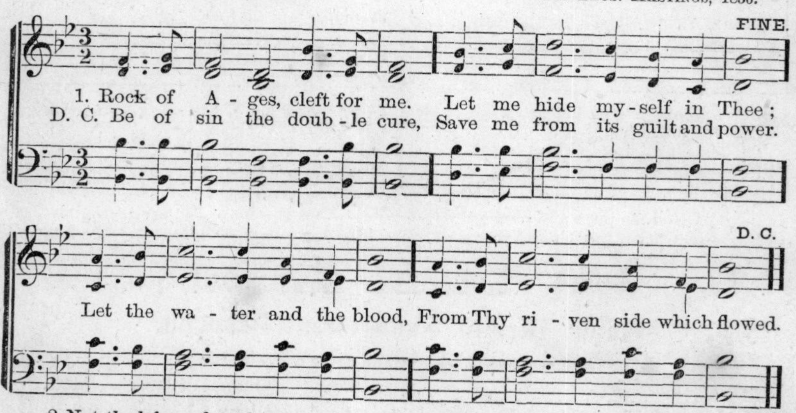
FINE.
1. Rock of A - ges, cleft for me. Let me hide my-self in Thee;
D. C. Be of sin the doub - le cure, Save me from its guilt and power.
D. C.
Let the wa - ter and the blood, From Thy ri - ven side which flowed.

2 Not the labor of my hands
Can fulfil Thy law's demands;
Could my zeal no respite know,
Could my tears forever flow,
All for sin could not atone;
Thou must save, and Thou alone.

3 Nothing in my hand I bring,
Simply to Thy cross I cling;
Naked, come to Thee for dress,
Helpless, look to Thee for grace;
Foul, I to the fountain fly,
Wash me, Saviour, or I die.

4 While I draw this fleeting breath,
When mine eyes shall close in death,
When I soar to worlds unknown,
See Thee on Thy judgment throne,—
Rock of Ages, cleft for me,
Let me hide myself in Thee.

No. 87. Even Me.

"Bless me, even me also, O my Father."—GEN. 27: 38.

Mrs. ELIZ. CODNER. WM. B. BRADBURY, by per.

1. Lord, I hear of showers of bless-ing Thou art scattering full and free—
2, Pass me not, O gracious Fa-ther! Sin - ful tho' my heart may be;
3. Pass me not, O ten-der Saviour! Let me love and cling to Thee;
Showers, the thirsty land re - freshing; Let some droppings fall on me—
Thou might'st leave me, but the rath - er Let Thy mer - cy fall on me—
I am long-ing for Thy fa - vor; Whilst Thou'rt calling, oh, call me—
E - ven me, E - ven me, Let Thy bless-ing fall on me.

4 Pass me not, O mighty Spirit!
Thou canst make the blind to see;
Witnesser of Jesus' merit,
Speak the word of power to me.–Even me.

5 Love of God, so pure and changeless;
Blood of Christ, so rich and free;
Grace of God, so strong and boundless;—
Magnify them all in me.—Even me.

6 Pass me not! Thy lost one bringing,
Bind my heart, O Lord, to Thee;
While the streams of life are springing,
Blessing others, oh, bless me.—Even me.

No. 88. Guide Me, O Thou Great Jehovah.

"For Thy name's sake, lead me and guide me."—PSALM 31: 3.

WILLIAM WILLIAMS, 1771.

1 Guide me, O Thou great Jehovah,
Pilgrim through this barren land;
I am weak, but Thou art mighty,
Hold me with Thy powerful hand:
Bread of heaven,
Feed me till I want no more.

2 Open now the crystal fountain,
Whence the healing waters flow;
Let the fiery, cloudy pillar
Lead me all my journey through:
Strong Deliverer,
Be Thou still my strength and shield.

3 When I tread the verge of Jordan,
Bid my anxious fears subside;
Bear me through the swelling current,
Land me safe on Canaan's side;
Songs of praises
I will ever give to Thee.

No. 89. Yield Not to Temptation.

"God is faithful, who will not suffer you to be tempted above that ye are able."—1 Cor. 10: 13.

H. R. Palmer. H. R. Palmer, by per.

1. Yield not to temp-ta - tion, For yielding is sin, Each vic - t'ry will
2. Shun e - vil com-pan-ions, Bad language dis - dain, God's name hold in
3. To him that o'ercom - eth God giv - eth a crown, Thro' faith we shall
help you Some oth - er to win; Fight man-ful - ly on - ward,
rev'rence, Nor take it in vain; Be thoughtful and earn - est,
con - quer, Though oft-en cast down; He who is our Sav - iour,
Dark passions sub-due, Look ev-er to Je - sus, He'll carry you through.
Kind-hearted and true, Look ev-er to Je - sus, He'll carry you through.
Our strength will renew, Look ev-er to Je - sus, He'll carry you through.
CHORUS.
Ask the Saviour to help you, Com-fort, strengthen, and keep you;
He is will-ing to aid you, He will car - ry you through.

No 90. I Left it All with Jesus.

"Casting all your care upon Him; for He careth for you."—1 PETER 5: 7.

Miss ELLEN H. WILLIS. English.

f
1. I left it all with Je - sus Long a - go; All my sins I brought Him,
2. I leave it all with Je - sus, For He knows How to steal the bit - ter
And my woe. When by faith I saw Him On the tree, Heard His small, still whisper,
From life's woes; How to gild the tear-drop With His smile, Make the desert garden
'Tis for thee,' From my heart the burden Rolled a - way— Hap - py day!
Bloom a-while: When my weakness leaneth On His might, All seems light.
Cres.
Rit.
From my heart the bur - den Rolled a - way— Hap - py day!
When my weakness lean - eth On His might, All seems light.

3 I leave it all with Jesus
Day by day;
Faith can firmly trust Him
Come what may.
Hope has dropped her anchor,
Found her rest
In the calm, sure haven
Of His breast:
Love esteems it heaven
To abide At His side.

4 Oh, leave it *all* with Jesus,
Drooping soul!
Tell not *half* thy story,
But the whole.
Worlds on worlds are hanging
On His hand,
Life and death are waiting
His command;
Yet His tender bosom
Makes *thee* room—Oh, come home!

No. 91. There is a Fountain.

"A Fountain opened for sin."—ZECH. 13: 1.

WM. COWPER, 1779. WESTERN MELODY.

1. There is a fountain filled with blood, Drawn from Immanuel's veins,
2. The dy - ing thief re - joiced to see That fountain in his day;
And sin - ners plunged beneath that flood Lose all their guil - ty stains,
And there may I, though vile as he, Wash all my sins a - way,
REFRAIN.
Lose all their guil - ty stains, Lose all their guil - ty stains;
Wash all my sins a - way, Wash all my sins a - way;
And sin - ners plunged beneath that flood Lose all their guil- ty stains.
And there may I, though vile as he, Wash all my sins a - way.

3

E'er since by faith I saw the stream
Thy flowing wounds supply,
Redeeming love has been my theme
And shall be till I die. *Ref.*

4

Then in a nobler, sweeter song
I'll sing thy power to save, [tongue
When this poor, lisping, stammering
Lies silent in the grave. *Ref.*

No. 92. The Home Over There.

"Oh that I had wings like a dove, for then would I fly away and be at rest."—PSALM 55: 6.

Rev. D. W. C. HUNTINGTON. TULLIUS C. O'KANE, by per.

1. Oh, think of the home over there, By the side of the river of light, Where the
2. Oh, think of the friends over there, Who before us the journey have trod, Of the
over there,
saints, all immor-tal and fair, Are robed in their garments of white, over there.
songs that they breathe on the air, In their home in the palace of God, over there.
REFRAIN.
Over there, over there, Oh, think of the home over there, over there; Over
Over there, over there, Oh, think of the friends over there, over there; Over
over there,
over there,
over there,
there, over there, over there, o - ver there, Oh, think of the home o - ver there.
there, over there, over there, o - ver there, Oh, think of the friends o-ver there.
over there,

3 My Saviour is now over there,
There my kindred and friends are at rest;
Then away from my sorrow and care,
Let me fly to the land of the blest.
Over there, over there,
My Saviour is now over there.

4 I'll soon be at home over there,
For the end of my journey I see;
Many dear to my heart, over there,
Are watching and waiting for me.
Over there, over there,
I'll soon be at home over there.

No. 93.

My Prayer.

"Be ye therefore perfect."—MATT. 5: 8.

P. P. BLISS. P. P. BLISS, by per.

1. More ho - li - ness give me, More striv - ings with - in;
2. More grat - i - tude give me, More trust in the Lord;
3. More pu - ri - ty give me, More strength to o'er - come;
More pa - tience in suff - 'ring, More sor - row for sin;
More pride in His glo - ry, More hope in His word;
More free - dom from earth - stains, More long - ings for home;
More faith in my Sav - iour, More sense of His care;
More tears for His sor - rows, More pain at His grief;
More fit for the king - dom, More used would I be;
Rit.
More joy in His ser - vice, More pur - pose in prayer.
More meek-ness in tri - al, More praise for re - lief.
More bless - ed and ho - ly, More, Sav - iour, like Thee.

No. 94. Only Trust Him.

"Take My yoke upon you, and learn of Me; and ye shall find rest unto your souls."—MATT. 11: 29.

Rev. J. H. S. — Rev. J. H. STOCKTON, by per.

1. Come, ev - ery soul by sin oppressed, There's mercy with the Lord,
And He will sure - ly give you rest, By trust-ing in His word.
CHORUS.
On - ly trust Him, on - ly trust Him, On - ly trust Him now.
He will save you, He will save you, He will save you now.

2 For Jesus shed His precious blood
Rich blessings to bestow;
Plunge now into the crimson flood
That washes white as snow.

3 Yes, Jesus is the Truth, the Way,
That leads you into rest;
Believe in Him without delay,
And you are fully blest.

4 Come then, and join this holy band,
And on to glory go,
To dwell in that celestial land,
Where joys immortal flow.

No. 95. Yes, There is Pardon for You.

"He will abundantly pardon."—ISA. 55: 17.

FANNY J. CROSBY. HUBERT P. MAIN, by per.

Slowly.
1. Oh, come to the Sav-iour, be-lieve in His name, And ask Him your heart to re-new; He waits to be gra-cious, O turn not a-way, For now there is par-don for you.
2. The way of trans-gres-sion that leads un-to death, Oh, why will you long-er pur-sue? How can you re-ject the sweet mes-sage of love That of-fers full par-don for you?
3. Be warned of your dan-ger; es-cape to the cross; Your on-ly sal-va-tion is there; Be-lieve, and that moment the Spir-it of grace Will an-swer your pen-i-tent prayer.
CHORUS.
Yes, there is pardon for you,.... Yes, there is pardon for you;....
for you, for you,
For Je-sus has died to re-deem you, And of-fers full pardon to you.

No. 96.

Nothing but Leaves.

"And when He came to it He found nothing but leaves."—MARK 11: 13.

MRS. LUCY EVELINA AKERMAN.

SILAS J. VAIL, by per.

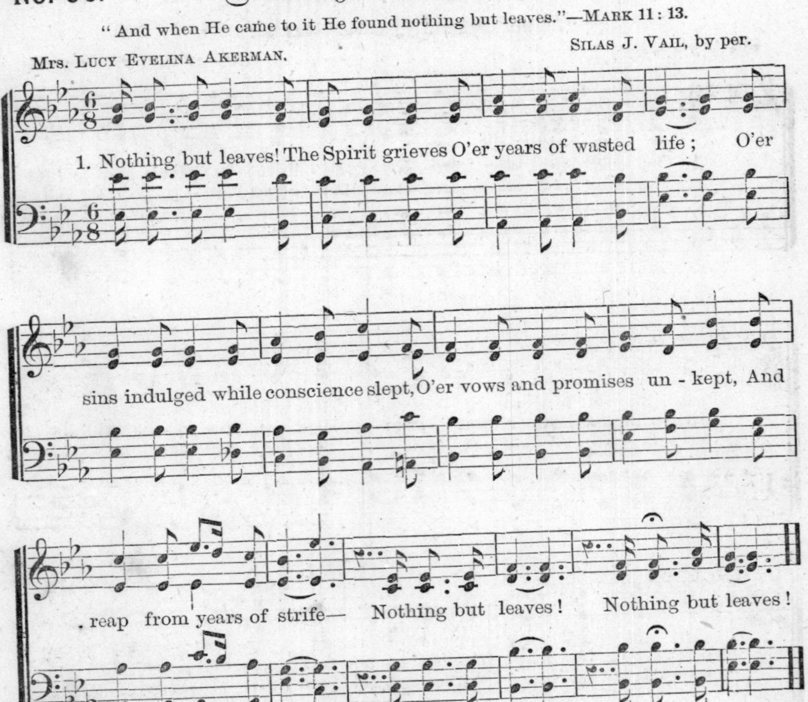
1. Nothing but leaves! The Spirit grieves O'er years of wasted life; O'er
sins indulged while conscience slept, O'er vows and promises un - kept, And
reap from years of strife— Nothing but leaves! Nothing but leaves!

2 Nothing but leaves! No gathered sheaves,
Of life's fair ripening grain:
We sow our seeds; lo! tares and weeds,—
Words, *idle* words, for earnest deeds—
Then reap, with toil and pain,
Nothing but leaves! nothing but leaves!

3 Nothing but leaves! Sad mem'ry weaves
No veil to hide the past:
And as we trace our weary way,
And count each lost and misspent day
We sadly find at last—
Nothing but leaves! nothing but leaves!

Ah, who shall thus the Master meet,
And bring but withered leaves?
Ah, who shall at the Saviour's feet,
Before the awful judgment-seat
Lay down for golden sheaves,
Nothing but leaves! nothing but leaves!

No. 97.

Jewels.

" And they shall be Mine, saith the Lord of hosts, in that day when I make up My jewels."—MALACHI 3: 17.

Rev. W. O. CUSHING.

GEO. F. ROOT, by per.

Moderato.
1. When He com - eth, when He com - eth To make up His
jew - els, All His jew-els, precious jewels, His loved and His own.
CHORUS.
Like the stars of the morn - ing, His bright crown a -
dorn - ing, They shall shine in their beauty, Bright gems for His crown.

2 He will gather, He will gather
The gems for His kingdom:
All the pure ones, all the bright ones,
His loved and His own. *Cho.*

3 Little children, little children,
Who love their Redeemer,
Are the jewels, precious jewels,
His loved and His own. *Cho.*

No. 98. Go Work in My Vineyard.

"Go work to-day in My vineyard."—MATT. 21: 28.

ANON. T. C. O'KANE, by per.

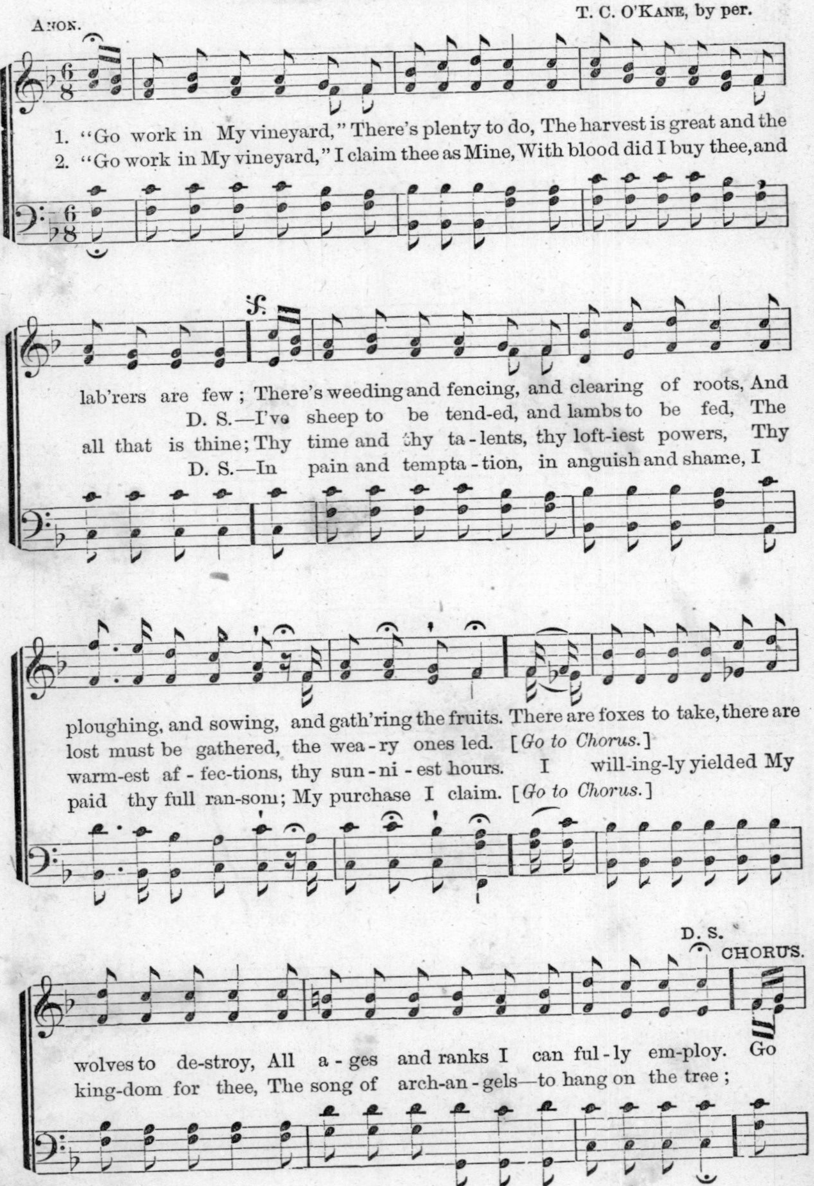
1. "Go work in My vineyard," There's plenty to do, The harvest is great and the lab'rers are few; There's weeding and fencing, and clearing of roots, And ploughing, and sowing, and gath'ring the fruits. There are foxes to take, there are wolves to de-stroy, All a-ges and ranks I can ful-ly em-ploy.
D. S.—I've sheep to be tend-ed, and lambs to be fed, The lost must be gathered, the wea-ry ones led. [Go to Chorus.]
2. "Go work in My vineyard," I claim thee as Mine, With blood did I buy thee, and all that is thine; Thy time and thy ta-lents, thy loft-iest powers, Thy warm-est af-fec-tions, thy sun-ni-est hours. I will-ing-ly yielded My king-dom for thee, The song of arch-an-gels—to hang on the tree;
D. S.—In pain and tempta-tion, in anguish and shame, I paid thy full ran-som; My purchase I claim. [Go to Chorus.]
D. S.
CHORUS.
Go

Go Work in My Vineyard.—Concluded.

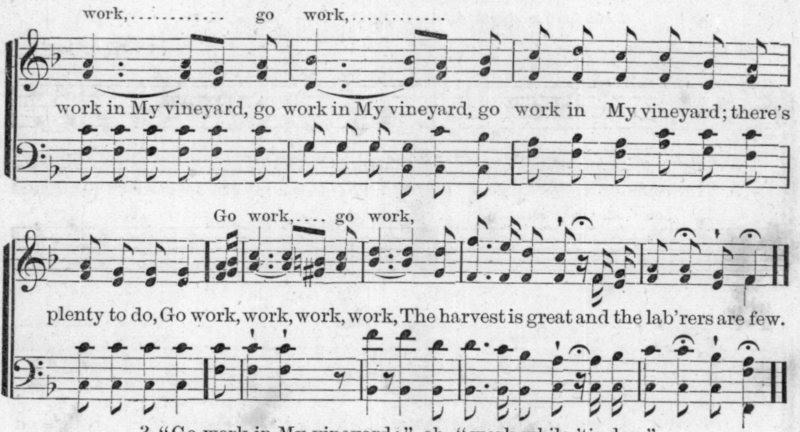
work,............ go work,............
work in My vineyard, go work in My vineyard, go work in My vineyard; there's
Go work,.... go work,
plenty to do, Go work, work, work, work, The harvest is great and the lab'rers are few.

3 "Go work in My vineyard;" oh, "work while 'tis day,"
The bright hours of sunshine are hastening away;
And night's gloomy shadows are gathering fast;
Then the time for our labor shall ever be past.
Begin in the morning, and toil all the day,
Thy strength I'll supply and thy wages I'll pay;
And blessed, thrice blessed the diligent few,
Who finish the labor I've given them to do.

No. 99.

Seymour. 7s.

"A broken and a contrite heart, O God, thou wilt not despise."—Ps. 51 : 17.

Rev. Chas. Wesley, 1740. C. M. Von Weber.

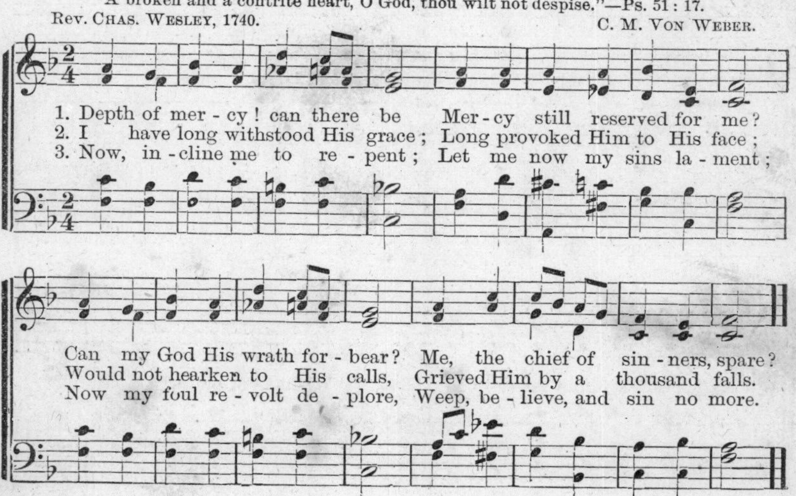
1. Depth of mer - cy! can there be Mer - cy still reserved for me?
2. I have long withstood His grace; Long provoked Him to His face;
3. Now, in - cline me to re - pent; Let me now my sins la - ment;
Can my God His wrath for - bear? Me, the chief of sin - ners, spare?
Would not hearken to His calls, Grieved Him by a thousand falls.
Now my foul re - volt de - plore, Weep, be - lieve, and sin no more.

No. 100. When the Comforter Came.

"He shall give you another Comforter."—JOHN. 14: 16.

WILLIAM MOORE. Rev. R. LOWRY, by per.

1. My heart, that was heavy and sad, Was made to re - joice and be glad.
2. To sin and to e - vil in-clined, With darkness per-vad-ing my mind,
3. The voice of thanksgiving I raised, The Lord, my Re-deem-er I praised;

And peace without measure I had, When the Com - fort - er came.
No rest I could a - ny-where find, Till the Com - fort - er came.
I was at His mer - cy a - maz'd, When the Com - fort - er came.

REFRAIN.

Peace, sweet peace, Peace when the Comfort-er came! My heart that was

heav - y and sad, Was made to re - joice and be glad,

And peace without measure I had, When the Comfort - er came.

No. 101. Coronation. C. M.

Rev. E. PERRONET, 1780. O. HOLDEN, 1793.

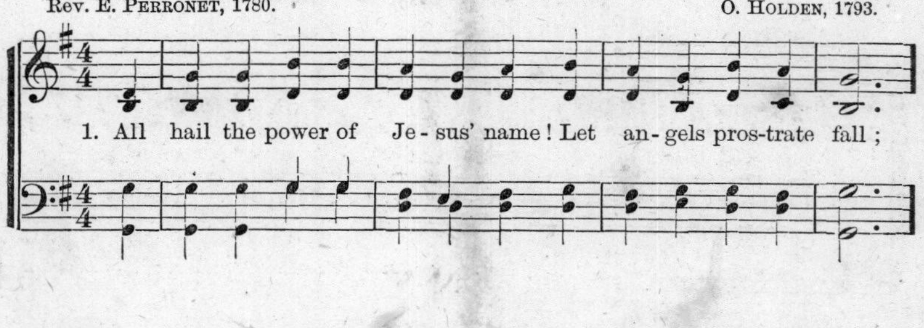
1. All hail the power of Je - sus' name! Let an-gels pros-trate fall;

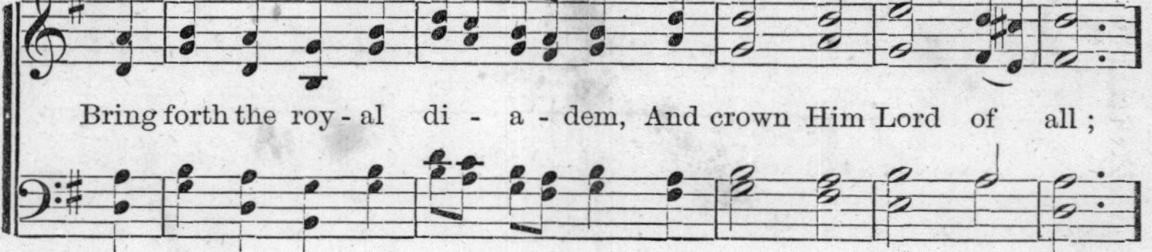
Bring forth the roy - al di - a - dem, And crown Him Lord of all;

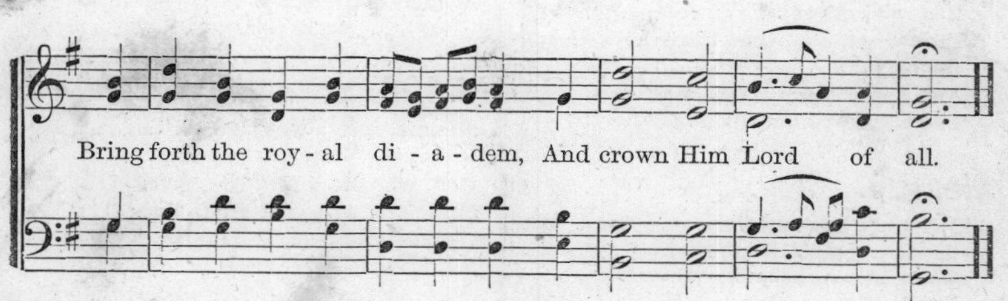
Bring forth the roy - al di - a - dem, And crown Him Lord of all.

2 Let every kindred, every tribe,
On this terrestrial ball,
To Him all majesty ascribe,
And crown Him Lord of all.

3 Oh, that with yonder sacred throng
We at His feet may fall;
We'll join the everlasting song,
And crown Him Lord of all.

No. 102.

1 O for a thousand tongues to sing
My great Redeemer's praise;
The glories of my God and King,
The triumphs of His grace.

2 My gracious Master, and my God,
Assist me to proclaim,—
To spread, through all the earth abroad,
The honors of Thy Name.

3 Jesus!—the Name that charms our fears
That bids our sorrows cease;
'Tis music in the sinner's ears,
'Tis life, and health, and peace.

4 He breaks the power of cancell'd sin,
He sets the pris'ner free;
His blood can make the foulest clean;
His blood avail'd for me.

Rev. CHAS. WESLEY, 1740.

No. 103. Rockingham. L. M.

WM. COWPER, 1779. DR. LOWELL MASON, 1832.

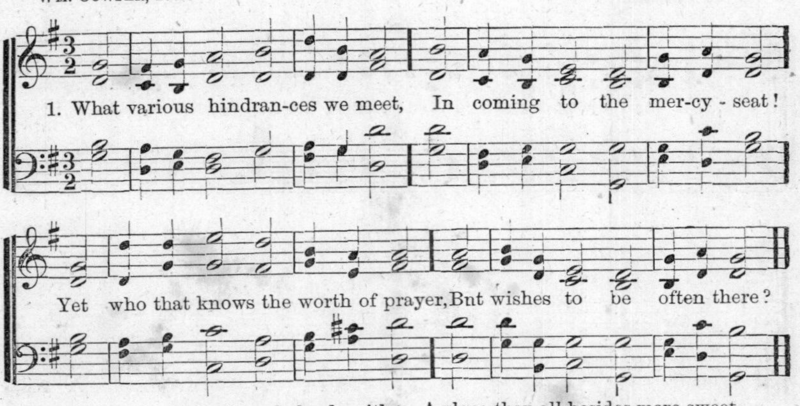
1. What various hindran-ces we meet, In coming to the mer-cy - seat!
Yet who that knows the worth of prayer, But wishes to be often there?

2 Prayer makes the darkened clouds withdraw;
Prayer climbs the ladder Jacob saw,
Gives exercise to faith and love,
Brings every blessing from above.

3 Restraining prayer, we cease to fight;
Prayer makes the Christian's armor bright;
And Satan trembles when he sees
The weakest saint upon his knees.

No. 104. L. M.

1 So let our lips and lives express
The holy gospel we profess;
So let our works and virtues shine,
To prove the doctrine all divine.

2 Thus shall we best proclaim abroad
The honors of our Saviour God;
When His salvation reigns within,
And grace subdues the power of sin.

3 Religion bears our spirits up,
While we expect that blessed hope,—
The bright appearance of the Lord:
And faith stands leaning on His word.

REV. I. WATTS, 1709.

No. 105. RETREAT. L. M. Key C.

1 From every stormy wind that blows,
From every swelling tide of woes,
There is a calm, a sure retreat;
'Tis found beneath the mercy-seat.

2 There is a place, where Jesus sheds
The oil of gladness on our heads;
A place than all besides more sweet,—
It is the blood-bought mercy-seat.

3 There is a scene where spirits blend,
Where friend holds fellowship with friend;
Though sunder'd far, by faith we meet,
Around one common mercy-seat.

REV. HUGH STOWELL, 1827.

No. 106. BENEVENTO. 7s. 8 lines. Key F.

1 Sinners, turn; why will ye die?
God, your Maker, asks you why?
God, who did your being give,
Made you with himself to live;
He the fatal cause demands;
Asks the work of His own hands,—
Why, ye thankless creatures, why
Will ye cross His love, and die?

2 Sinners, turn; why will ye die?
God, your Saviour, asks you why?
He, who did your souls retrieve,
Died Himself, that ye might live.
Will ye let Him die in vain?
Crucify your Lord again?
Why, ye ransomed sinners, why
Will ye slight His grace and die?

3 Sinners, turn; why will ye die?
God, the Spirit, asks you why?
He who all your lives hath strove,
Urged you to embrace His love.
Will ye not His grace receive?
Will ye still refuse to live?
O ye dying sinners, why,
Why will ye forever die?

REV. C. WESLEY, 1745.

No. 107. Evan. C. M.

"Rouse's Version," 1643. PSALM 23. WM. H. HAVERGAL, 1847.

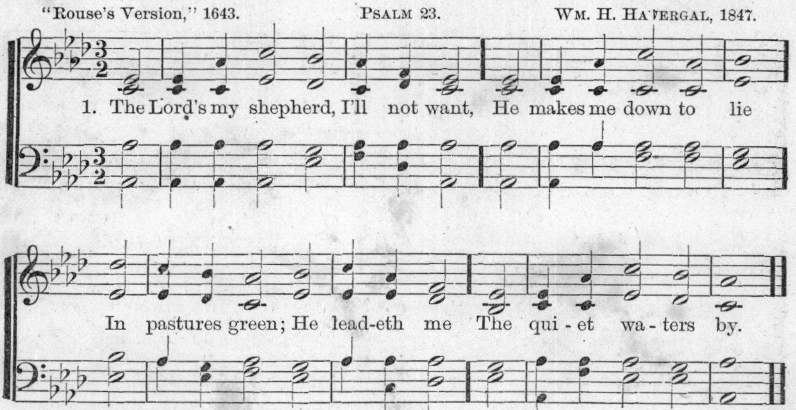
1. The Lord's my shepherd, I'll not want, He makes me down to lie
In pastures green; He lead-eth me The qui - et wa - ters by.

2 My soul He doth restore again,
And me to walk doth make
Within the paths of righteousness,
Ev'n for His own name's sake.

3 Yea, though I walk in death's dark vale,
Yet will I fear none ill;
For Thou art with me; and Thy rod
And staff me comfort still.

4 My table Thou hast furnished
In presence of my foes;
My head Thou dost with oil anoint,
And my cup overflows.

5 Goodness and mercy all my life
Shall surely follow me;
And in God's house for evermore,
My dwelling place shall be.

No. 108. C. M.

1 O for a faith that will not shrink,
Though press'd by every foe,
That will not tremble on the brink
Of any earthly wo;

2 That will not murmur or complain
Beneath the chast'ning rod,
But, in the hour of grief or pain,
Will lean upon its God;—

3 A faith that shines more bright and clear
When tempests rage without;
That when in danger knows no fear,
In darkness feels no doubt;—

4 Lord, give us such a faith as this,
And then, whate'er may come,
We'll taste, e'en here, the hallow'd bliss
Of an eternal home.

Rev. W. H. BATHURST, 1831.

No. 109. AZMON. L. M. Key A.

1 Salvation! O the joyful sound!
What pleasure to our ears;
A sovereign balm for every wound,
A cordial for our fears.

2 Salvation! let the echo fly
The spacious earth around,
While all the armies of the sky
Conspire to raise the sound.

3 Salvation! O Thou bleeding Lamb!
To Thee the praise belongs:
Salvation shall inspire our hearts,
And dwell upon our tongues.

Rev. I. WATTS, 1709.

No. 110. ANTIOCH. Key E♭.

1 Joy to the world, the Lord is come!
Let earth receive her King;
Let every heart prepare Him room,
And heaven and nature sing.

2 Joy to the world, the Saviour reigns,
Let men their songs employ;
While fields and floods, rocks, hills, and
Repeat the sounding joy. [plains,

3 He rules the world with truth and grace,
And makes the nations prove
The glories of His righteousness,
And wonders of His love.

Rev. I. WATTS, 1719.

No. 111. Dundee. C. M.

Rev. Isaac Watts, 1709. Guillaume Franc, 1545.

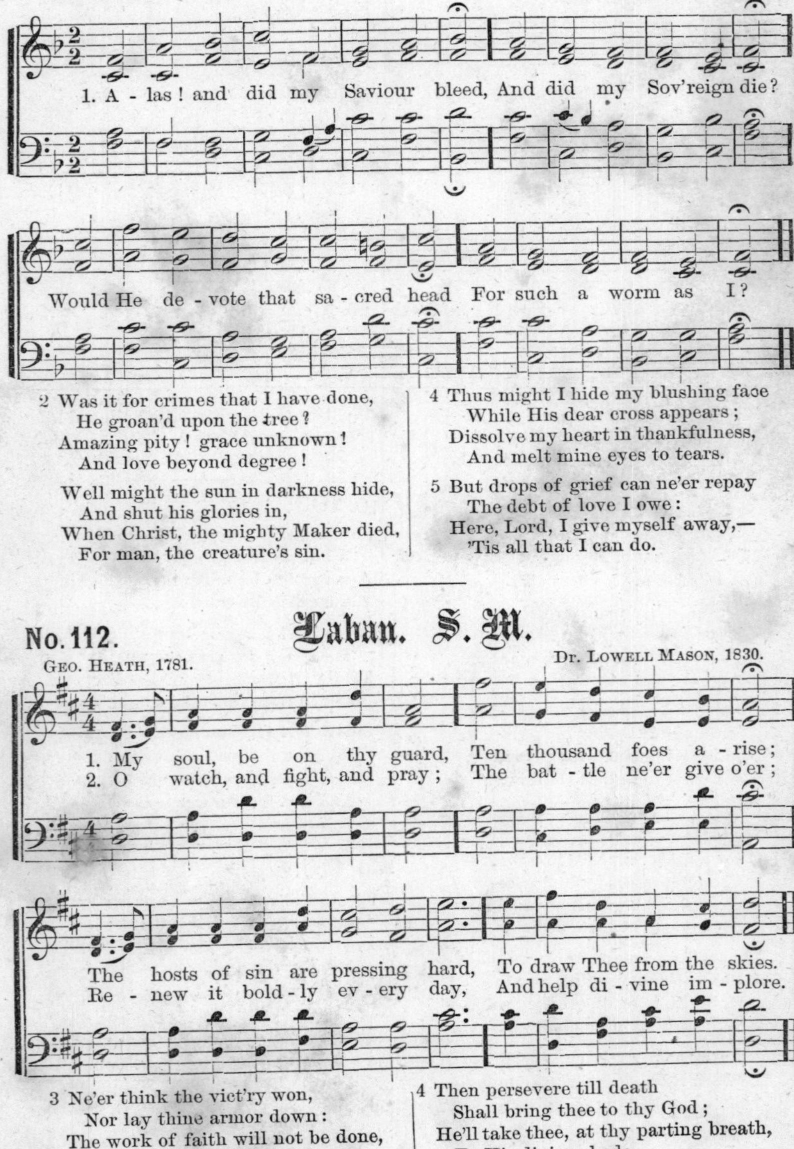
1. A - las! and did my Saviour bleed, And did my Sov'reign die?
Would He de - vote that sa - cred head For such a worm as I?
1. My soul, be on thy guard, Ten thousand foes a - rise;
2. O watch, and fight, and pray; The bat - tle ne'er give o'er;
The hosts of sin are pressing hard, To draw Thee from the skies.
Re - new it bold - ly ev - ery day, And help di - vine im - plore.

2 Was it for crimes that I have done,
He groan'd upon the tree?
Amazing pity! grace unknown!
And love beyond degree!

Well might the sun in darkness hide,
And shut his glories in,
When Christ, the mighty Maker died,
For man, the creature's sin.

4 Thus might I hide my blushing face
While His dear cross appears;
Dissolve my heart in thankfulness,
And melt mine eyes to tears.

5 But drops of grief can ne'er repay
The debt of love I owe:
Here, Lord, I give myself away,—
'Tis all that I can do.

No. 112. Laban. S. M.

Geo. Heath, 1781. Dr. Lowell Mason, 1830.

3 Ne'er think the vict'ry won,
Nor lay thine armor down:
The work of faith will not be done,
Till thou obtain the crown.

4 Then persevere till death
Shall bring thee to thy God;
He'll take thee, at thy parting breath,
To His divine abode.

No. 113. Boylston. S. M.

Rev. Isaac Watts, 1709. Dr. Lowell Mason, 1832.

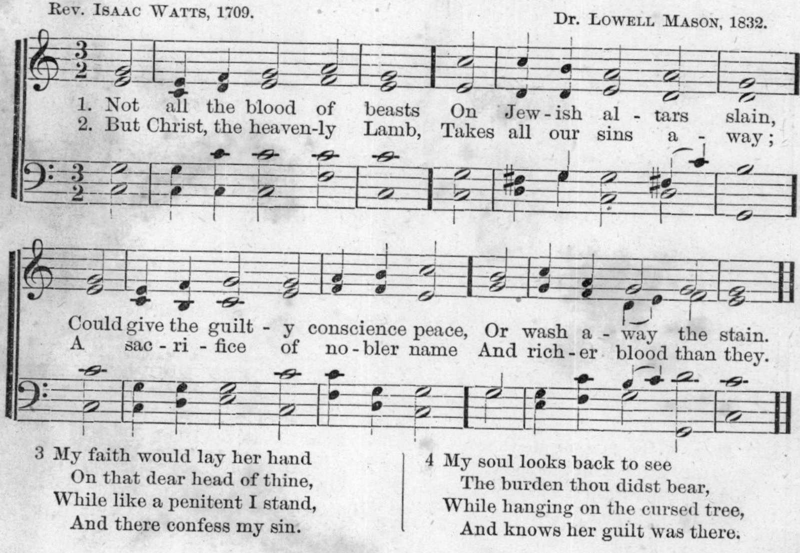
1. Not all the blood of beasts On Jew-ish al-tars slain,
2. But Christ, the heaven-ly Lamb, Takes all our sins a-way;
Could give the guilt-y conscience peace, Or wash a-way the stain.
A sac-ri-fice of no-bler name And rich-er blood than they.

3 My faith would lay her hand
On that dear head of thine,
While like a penitent I stand,
And there confess my sin.

4 My soul looks back to see
The burden thou didst bear,
While hanging on the cursed tree,
And knows her guilt was there.

No. 114. Dennis. S. M

Rev. John Fawcett, 1772. From H. G. Nageli.

1. Blest be the tie that binds Our hearts in Christ-ian love;
2. Be-fore our Fa-ther's throne, We pour our ar-dent prayers;
The fel-low-ship of kin-dred minds Is like to that a-bove.
Our fears, our hopes, our aims are one,— Our com-forts and our cares.

3 We share our mutual woes;
Our mutual burdens bear;
And often for each other flows
The sympathizing tear.

4 When we asunder part,
It gives us inward pain;
But we shall still be join'd in heart,
And hope to meet again.

No. 115. Arlington. C. M.

Rev. Isaac Watts, 1720. Thos. A. Arne, 1744.

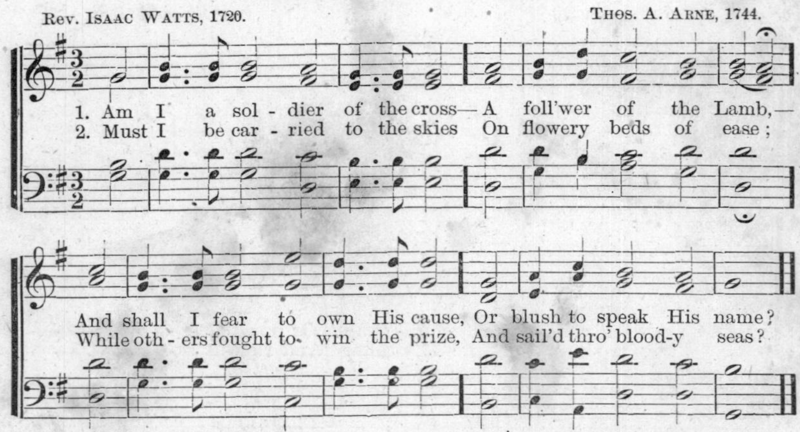
1. Am I a sol - dier of the cross—A foll'wer of the Lamb,—
2. Must I be car - ried to the skies On flowery beds of ease;
And shall I fear to own His cause, Or blush to speak His name?
While oth - ers fought to win the prize, And sail'd thro' blood-y seas?

3 Are there no foes for me to face?
Must I not stem the flood?
Is this vile world a friend to grace,
To help me on to God?

4 Since I must fight if I would reign,
Increase my courage, Lord;
I'll bear the toil, endure the pain,
Supported by Thy word.

No. 116. Nettleton. 8s & 7s.

Rev. R. Robinson, 1758. Old Melody, 1812.

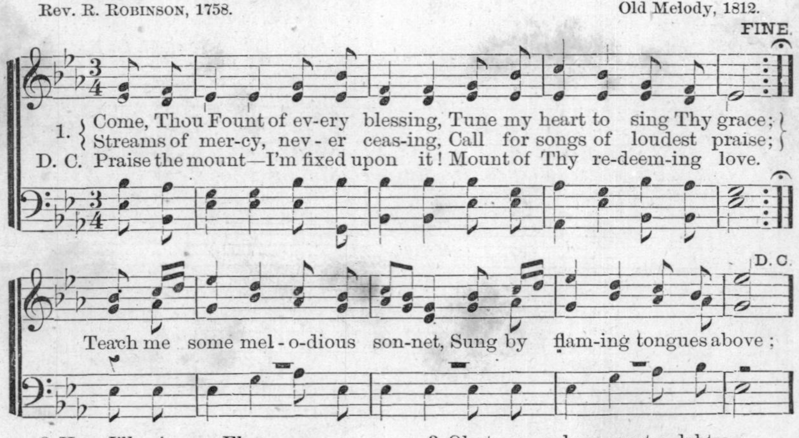
FINE.
1. { Come, Thou Fount of ev-ery blessing, Tune my heart to sing Thy grace; }
{ Streams of mer-cy, nev - er ceas-ing, Call for songs of loudest praise; }
D. C. Praise the mount—I'm fixed upon it! Mount of Thy re-deem-ing love.
D. C.
Teach me some mel - o-dious son-net, Sung by flam-ing tongues above;

2 Here I'll raise my Ebenezer,
Hither by Thy help I'm come;
And I hope by Thy good pleasure,
Safely to arrive at home.
Jesus sought me when a stranger,
Wandering from the fold of God;
He to rescue me from danger,
Interposed His precious blood.

3 Oh, to grace how great a debtor,
Daily I'm constrained to be!
Let Thy goodness as a fetter,
Bind my wandering heart to Thee;
Prone to wander, Lord, I feel it—
Prone to leave the God I love—
Here's my heart, oh, take and seal it,
Seal it for Thy courts above.

No. 117. New Haven. 6s & 4s.

Rev. Ray Palmer, D. D. 1830. Dr. Thos. Hastings, 1833.

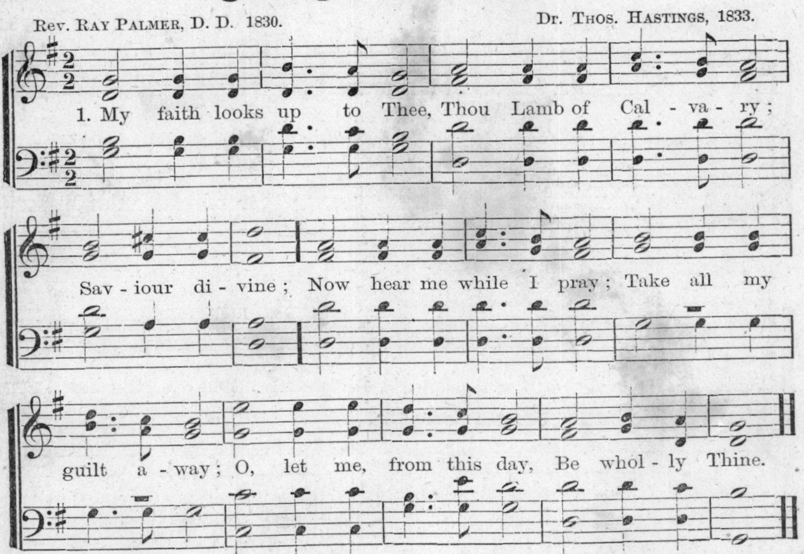
1. My faith looks up to Thee, Thou Lamb of Cal - va - ry;
Sav - iour di - vine; Now hear me while I pray; Take all my
guilt a - way; O, let me, from this day, Be whol - ly Thine.

2 May Thy rich grace impart
Strength to my fainting heart;
My zeal inspire;
As Thou hast died for me,
O may my love to Thee
Pure, warm, and changeless be—
A living fire.

3 While life's dark maze I tread,
And griefs around me spread,
Be Thou my guide;
Bid darkness turn to day;
Wipe sorrow's tears away,
Nor let me ever stray
From Thee aside.

4 When ends life's transient dream;
When death's cold sullen stream
Shall o'er me roll;
Blest Saviour, then in love,
Fear and distress remove;
O bear me safe above,—
A ransom'd soul.

No. 118. Bethany. 6s & 4s. Key G.

1 Nearer, my God, to Thee,
Nearer to Thee!
E'en though it be a cross
That raiseth me;
Still all my song shall be—
Nearer, my God, to Thee!
Nearer to Thee!

2 Though, like the wanderer,
The sun gone down,
Darkness be over me,
My rest a stone;
Yet in my dreams I'd be—
Nearer, my God, to Thee!
Nearer to Thee!

3 There let the way appear,
Steps unto heaven;
All that Thou sendest me,
In mercy given;
Angels to beckon me
Nearer, my God, to Thee—
Nearer to Thee!

4 Then with my waking thoughts,
Bright with Thy praise,
Out of my stony griefs,
Bethel I'll raise;
So by my woes to be
Nearer, my God, to Thee!
Nearer to Thee!

5 Or if on joyful wing,
Cleaving the sky,
Sun moon, and stars forgot,
Upward I fly;
Still all my song shall be—
Nearer, my God, to Thee!
Nearer to Thee!

Mrs. Sarah F. Adams, 1840.

No. 119. Lenox. 6s & 8s.

Rev. Ch. Wesley, 1742. J. Edson, 1782.

1. A-rise, my soul, a-rise ; Shake off thy guilty fears The bleeding sacri-fice
In my be-half ap-pears ; Be-fore the throne my Surety stands,
My name is written on His hands, My name is written on His hands.

2 He ever lives above,
For me to intercede,
His all redeeming love,
His precious blood to plead ;
His blood atoned for all our race,
And sprinkles now the throne of grace.

3 Five bleeding wounds He bears,
Received on Calvary;
They pour effectual prayers,
They strongly plead for me ;
Forgive him, oh, forgive, they cry,
Nor let that ransomed sinner die.

4 My God is reconciled ;
His pardoning voice I hear ;
He owns me for His child ;
I can no longer fear ;
With confidence I now draw nigh,
And Father, Abba, Father, cry.

No. 120. "Your Mission." Key F.

1 Hark! the voice of Jesus crying,—
"Who will go and work to-day?
Fields are white and harvest waiting ;
Who will bear the sheaves away?"
Loud and strong the Master calleth,
Rich reward He offers thee :
Who will answer, gladly saying,
"Here am I; send me, send me!"

2 If you cannot cross the ocean,
And the heathen lands explore,
You can find the heathen nearer,
You can help them at your door.
If you cannot give your thousands,
You can give the widow's mite ;
And the least you do for Jesus,
Will be precious in His sight.

No. 120.—*Concluded.*

3 If you cannot speak like angels,
If you cannot preach like Paul,
You can tell the love of Jesus,
You can say He died for all.
If you cannot rouse the wicked
With the judgment's dread alarms,
You can lead the little children
To the Saviour's waiting arms.

4 If you cannot be the watchman,
Standing high on Zion's wall,
Pointing out the path to heaven,
Offering life and peace to all;
With your prayers and with your bounties
You can do what heaven demands;
You can be like faithful Aaron,
Holding up the prophet's hands.

5 If among the older people,
You may not be apt to teach; [herd,
"Feed my lambs," said Christ, our Shep-
"Place the food within their reach."
And it may be that the children
You have led with trembling hand,
Will be found among your jewels,
When you reach the better land.

6 Let none hear you idly saying,
"There is nothing I can do,"
While the souls of men are dying,
And the Master calls for you.
Take the task He gives you gladly,
Let His work your pleasure be;
Answer quickly when He calleth,
"Here am I; send me, send me!"

Rev. Dan'l. March, 1869.

No. 121.

WEBB. 7s & 6s.
Key B♭.

1 Stand up! stand up for Jesus!
Ye soldiers of the cross;
Lift high His royal banner,
It must not suffer loss;
From victory unto victory
His army He shall lead,
Till every foe is vanquished,
And Christ is Lord indeed.

2 Stand up! stand up for Jesus!
Stand in His strength alone;
The arm of flesh will fail you—
Ye dare not trust your own;
Put on the gospel armor,
And, watching unto prayer,
Where duty calls, or danger,
Be never wanting there.

3 Stand up! stand up for Jesus!
The strife will not be long;
This day the noise of battle,
The next the victor's song;
To him that overcometh,
A crown of life shall be;
He with the King of Glory
Shall reign eternally.

Rev. Geo. Duffield, Jr., 1858.

No. 122.

TUNE.—WORK, FOR THE NIGHT.
Key F.

1 Work, for the night is coming;
Work through the morning hours;
Work, while the dew is sparkling;
Work, 'mid springing flowers;
Work, when the day grows brighter,
Work, in the glowing sun;
Work, for the night is coming,
When man's work is done.

2 Work, for the night is coming;
Work through the sunny noon;
Fill brightest hours with labor;
Rest comes sure and soon.
Give every flying minute
Something to keep in store;
Work, for the night is coming,
When man works no more.

3 Work, for the night is coming,
Under the sunset skies;
While their bright tints are glowing,
Work, for daylight flies.
Work, till the last beam fadeth,
Fadeth to shine no more:
Work, while the night is dark'ning,
When man's work is o'er.

Arr. from Rev. S. Dyer, 1864.

No. 123.

EVAN. C.M.
Key A♭.

1 I heard the voice of Jesus say,
"Come unto Me and rest;
Lay down, thou weary one, lay down
Thy head upon My breast."

2 I came to Jesus as I was—
Weary, and worn, and sad;
I found in Him a resting-place,
And He has made me glad.

3 I heard the voice of Jesus say,
"Behold I freely give
The living water—thirsty one,
Stoop down, and drink, and live."

4 I came to Jesus, and I drank
Of that life-giving stream;
My thirst was quench'd, my soul revived,
And now I live in Him.

5 I heard the voice of Jesus say,
"I am this dark world's light,
Look unto Me, thy morn shall rise,
And all thy day be bright."

6 I look'd to Jesus, and I found
In Him my Star, my Sun;
And in that light of life I'll walk
'Till trav'ling days are done.

Rev. H. Bonar, 1857

No. 124. THE BEAUTIFUL RIVER.
Key E♭.

1 Shall we gather at the river
Where bright angel feet have trod;
With its crystal tide for ever
Flowing by the throne of God?
CHO.—Yes, we'll gather at the river,
The beautiful, the beautiful river—
Gather with the saints at the river,
That flows by the throne of God.

2 On the margin of the river,
Washing up its silver spray,
We will walk and worship ever,
All the happy golden day.—*Cho.*

3 Ere we reach the shining river,
Lay we every burden down;
Grace our spirits will deliver,
And provide a robe and crown.—*Cho.*

4 At the smiling of the river,
Mirror of the Saviour's face,
Saints whom death will never sever,
Lift their songs of saving grace.—*Cho.*

5 Soon we'll reach the silver river,
Soon our pilgrimage will cease;
Soon our happy hearts will quiver
With the melody of peace.—*Cho.*
REV. ROBERT LOWRY, 1864.

No. 125. 40th PSALM. C. M.

1 I waited for the Lord my God,
And patiently did bear;
At length to me He did incline
My voice and cry to hear.

2 He took me from a fearful pit,
And from the miry clay,
And on a rock He set my feet,
Establishing my way.

3 He put a new song in my mouth,
Our God to magnify;
Many shall see it, and shall fear,
And on the Lord rely.

4 O blessed is the man whose trust
Upon the Lord relies;
Respecting not the proud, nor such
As turn aside to lies.
SCOTCH VERSION.

No. 126. SAVIOUR, LIKE A SHEPHERD.
8s, 7s & 4. Key E♭.

1 Saviour, like a shepherd lead us,
Much we need Thy tend'rest care,
In Thy pleasant pastures feed us
For our use Thy folds prepare;
||: Blessed Jesus, blessed Jesus,
Thou hast bought us, Thine we are. :||

2 We are Thine, do Thou befriend us,
Be the Guardian of our way;
Keep Thy flock, from sin defend us,
Seek us when we go astray;
||: Blessed Jesus, blessed Jesus,
Hear, O hear us, when we pray. :||

3 Thou hast promised to receive us,
Poor and sinful though we be;
Thou hast mercy to relieve us,
Grace to cleanse, and power to free;
||: Blessed Jesus, blessed Jesus,
We will early turn to Thee. :||

4 Early let us seek Thy favor,
Early let us do Thy will;
Blessed Lord and only Saviour,
With Thy love our bosoms fill.
||: Blessed Jesus, blessed Jesus,
Thou hast loved us, love us still. :||
DOROTHY THRUPP, 1838.

No. 127. ZION. 8s, 7s & 4.
Key D.

1 Come, ye sinners, poor and needy,
Weak and wounded, sick and sore;
Jesus ready stands to save you,
Full of pity, love, and power:
||: He is able,
He is willing: doubt no more. :||

2 Now, ye needy, come and welcome;
God's free bounty glorify;
True belief and true repentance,—
Every grace that brings you nigh,—
||: Without money,
Come to Jesus Christ and buy. :||

3 Let not conscience make you linger;
Nor of fitness fondly dream:
All the fitness He requireth
Is to feel your need of Him:
||: This He gives you,—
'Tis the Spirit's glimm'ring beam. :||

4 Come, ye weary, heavy-laden,
Bruised and mangled by the fall;
If you tarry 'till you're better,
You will never come at all;
||: Not the righteous,—
Sinners, Jesus came to call. :||
REV. JOS. HART, 1759.

No. 128. C. M.

1 Come, Holy Spirit, Heavenly Dove!
With all Thy quickening powers;
Kindle a flame of heavenly love
In these cold hearts of ours.

2 Dear Lord! and shall we ever live
At this poor dying rate?
Our love so faint, so cold to Thee,
And Thine to us so great?

3 Come, Holy Spirit, Heavenly Dove,
With all Thy quickening powers;
Come, shed abroad a Saviour's love,
And that shall kindle ours.
I. WATTS, 1709.

No. 129. HE LOVED ME.

(Tune on page 23.)

1 Once I was dead in sin,
And hope within me died;
But now I'm dead to sin—
With Jesus crucified.

CHO.—And can it be that "He loved me,
And gave Himself for me?"

2 Oh height I can not reach,
Oh depth I can not sound,
Oh love, O boundless love,
In my Redeemer found! *Cho.*

3 Oh cold, ungrateful heart
That can from Jesus turn,
When living fires of love
Should on his altar burn. *Cho.*

4 I live—and yet, not I,
But Christ that lives in me;
Who from the law of sin
And death hath made me free. *Cho.*

REV. A. T. PIERSON.

No. 130. THE CHRISTIAN'S HOME. P. M.

Key C.

1 In the Christian's home in glory
There remains a land of rest;
There my Saviour's gone before me,
To fulfil my soul's request.

CHO.—||: There is rest for the weary, :||
There is rest for the weary,
There is rest for you;
On the other side of Jordan,
In the sweet fields of Eden,
Where the tree of life is blooming,
There is rest for you. *Cho.*

2 He is fitting up my mansion,
Which eternally shall stand;
For my stay shall not be transient
In that holy, happy land. *Cho.*

3 Sing, O sing, ye heirs of glory!
Shout your triumphs as you go;
Zion's gates will open for you,
You shall find an entrance through. *Cho.*

REV. SAM'L. Y. HARMER. 1856.

No. 131. BOYLSTON. S. M.

Key C.

1 Did Christ o'er sinners weep,
And shall our cheeks be dry?
Let floods of penitential grief
Burst forth from every eye.

2 The Son of God in tears
The wond'ring angels see;
Be thou astonish'd, O my soul;
He shed those tears for thee.

3 He wept that we might weep;
Each sin demands a tear:
In heaven alone no sin is found,
And there's no weeping there.

REV. BENJ. BEDDOME, 1787.

No. 132. COME TO JESUS.

Key F.

1 Come to Jesus, come to Jesus,
Come to Jesus just now;
Just now, come to Jesus,
Come to Jesus, just now.

2 He will save you, etc.

3 He is able, etc.

4 He is willing, etc.

5 He is waiting, etc.

6 He will hear you, etc.

7 He will cleanse you, etc.

8 He'll renew you, etc.

9 He'll forgive you, etc.

10 If you trust Him, etc.

11 He will save you, etc.

ENGLISH.

No. 133. HAPPY DAY. L. M.

Key G.

1 O happy day, that fixed my choice
On Thee, my Saviour and my God!
Well may this glowing heart rejoice,
And tell its raptures all abroad.

CHO.—Happy day, happy day,
When Jesus washed my sins away:
He taught me how to watch and pray,
And live rejoicing every day,
Happy day, happy day,
When Jesus washed my sins away.

2 'Tis done, the great transaction's done—
I am my Lord's, and He is mine;
He drew me, and I followed on,
Charmed to confess the voice divine. *Cho.*

3 Now rest, my long-divided heart;
Fixed on this blissful centre, rest;
Nor ever from thy Lord depart,
With Him of every good possessed. *Cho.*

4 High heaven, that heard the solemn vow,
That vow renewed shall daily hear,
Till in life's latest hour I bow,
And bless in death a bond so dear. *Cho.*

REV. P. DODDRIDGE, 1755.

INDEX.

Titles in Small Caps.—First Lines in Roman.

A. PAGE.

AH MY HEART 35
Ah my heart is heavy laden 35
Alas! and did my Saviour bleed 102
ALMOST PERSUADED 72
A long time I wandered 66
All hail the power of Jesus' name 99
ALL THE WAY MY SAVIOUR LEADS ME 60
All people that on earth do dwell 3
ALL TO CHRIST I OWE 36
Am I a soldier of the Cross 104
Arise my soul, arise! 106
ARLINGTON. C. M. 104
A SINNER FORGIVEN 64

B.

Beneath the cross of Jesus 44
BLESS ME NOW 33
Blest be the tie that binds 103
BOYLSTON. S. M. 103
Brightly beams our Father's mercy 65

C.

CALLING NOW 11
Come every soul, by sin oppressed 92
Come, Holy Spirit, heavenly Dove! 108
Come home, come home! 39
Come thou Fount of every blessing 104
Come to Jesus, come to Jesus! 109
COME TO THE SAVIOUR 62
Come ye sinners, poor and needy 108
CORONATION. C. M. 99
CROSS OF JESUS 44

D.

DENNIS. S. M. 103
Depth of mercy! can there be 97
Did Christ o'er sinners weep 109
Down life's dark vale we wander 53
DUNDEE. C. M. 102

E. PAGE.

EVAN. C. M. 101
EVEN ME 86
EVERY DAY AND HOUR 49

F.

Free from the law, oh happy 18
From every stormy wind that blows 100
FULLY PERSUADED 73

G.

GATE AJAR 17
GO BURY THY SORROW 61
God loved the world of sinners lost 31
GO WORK IN MY VINEYARD 96
Grace 'tis a charming sound 50
GREAT PHYSICIAN 56
Guide me, O Thou great Jehovah 86

H.

HALLELUJAH, 'TIS DONE! 4
Hark the voice of Jesus, crying 106
Have you on the Lord believed? 32
Heavenly Father, bless me now; 33
HE LEADETH ME 52
HOLD THE FORT 16
HOLY SPIRIT, FAITHFUL GUIDE! 41
HOME OF THE SOUL 22
HOME OVER THERE 90
Ho! my comrades, see the signal 16
How solemn are the words 68
How sweet the name of Jesus sounds 68

I.

I AM COMING TO THE CROSS 59
I AM PRAYING FOR YOU 13
I am so glad that our Father in 25
I am trusting, Lord, in Thee 59
I gave My life for thee 23

PAGE.
I have a Saviour, He's pleading in..... 13
I heard the voice of Jesus say 107
I hear the Saviour say.................. 36
I HEAR THY WELCOME VOICE........ 63
I know not the hour, when my Lord .. 15
I LEFT IT ALL WITH JESUS............ 88
I LOVE TO TELL THE STORY.......... 40
I NEED THEE EVERY HOUR........... 5
In some way or other, the Lord 7
In the Christian's home in glory 109
In the cross of Christ I glory.......... 67
IN THE PRESENCE OF THE KING 58
IT PASSETH KNOWLEDGE............. 70
I waited for the Lord, my God........ 108
I will sing you a song of that......... 22

J.

Jesus, keep me near the cross......... 46
JESUS LOVER OF MY SOUL............ 84
JESUS LOVES EVEN ME................. 25
JESUS OF NAZARETH PASSETH BY 10
JEWELS 95
Joy to the world, the Lord is come.... 101
JUST AS I AM.............................. 55
Just as I am, without one plea........ 55

K.

KNOCKING, KNOCKING, WHO IS THERE? 19

L.

LABAN. S. M............................ 102
LENOX. 6s & 8s......................... 106
LET THE LOWER LIGHTS BE BURNING 65
LIFE FOR A LOOK........................ 78
Light in the darkness, sailor, day..... 82
Lord, I hear of showers of blessing.... 86

M.

More holiness give me................. 91
MORE TO FOLLOW........................ 32
My faith looks up to Thee............. 105
My heart that was heavy and sad..... 98
MY PRAYER............................... 91
My soul, be on thy guard.............. 102

N.

Nearer, my God, to Thee.............. 105
NEAR THE CROSS 46
NETTLETON. 8s & 7s.................. 104
NEW HAVEN. 6s & 4s.................. 105
NEW SONG................................ 45
NINETY AND NINE 8
NO OTHER NAME........................ 75

PAGE
Not all the blood of beasts............ 103
NOTHING BUT LEAVES................. 94
NOT NOW MY CHILD.................... 48

O.

O Christ, what burdens bowed......... 57
O for a faith that will not shrink....... 101
O for a thousand tongues to sing....... 99
O happy day, that fixed my choice.... 109
Oh, bliss of the purified................. 47
Oh, come to the Saviour, believe....... 93
OH, HOW HE LOVES..................... 37
OH, SING OF HIS MIGHTY LOVE. 47
Oh, think of a home over there 90
OH, TO BE NOTHING.................... 71
Oh, to be over yonder 58
OLD HUNDRED. L. M................. 3
OLD, OLD STORY........................ 38
ONCE FOR ALL........................... 18
Once I was dead in sin................... 109
ONE MORE DAY'S WORK FOR JESUS.... 29
One offer of salvation.................. 75
One there is above all others.......... 37
ONLY AN ARMOUR BEARER........... 80
ONLY TRUST HIM 92

P.

PASS ME NOT 28
Pass me not, O gentle Saviour......... 28
Praise God, from whom all blessings.. 3
PRECIOUS NAME.......................... 69
PRECIOUS PROMISE..................... 51
Precious promise, God hath given 51
PRODIGAL CHILD........................ 39
PULL FOR THE SHORE.................. 82

R.

REJOICE AND BE GLAD................. 26
RESCUE THE PERISHING............... 20
REVIVE US AGAIN....................... 27
RING THE BELLS OF HEAVEN........ 21
ROCKINGHAM. L. M.................. 100
ROCK OF AGES.......................... 85

S.

SAFE IN THE ARMS OF JESUS......... 6
Salvation ! O the joyful sound......... 101
Saviour, like a Shepherd lead us...... 108
Saviour, more than life to me.......... 49
Saviour, Thy dying love................. 27
SEYMOUR. 7s............................ 97
Shall we gather at the river? 108

PAGE.

Sing of His Mighty Love 47
Sinners, turn, why will ye die? 100
So let our lives and lips express 100
Something for Jesus 27
Sowing the seed by the daylight fair .. 76
Stand up, stand up for Jesus.......... 107
Substitution 57
Sun of my Soul........................ 84
Sweet Hour of Prayer.............. 74

T.

Take the name of Jesus with you..... 69
Tell me the Old, Old Story 38
That will be Heaven for me 15
The Cross of Jesus................. 44
The Gate Ajar for me............. 17
The Great Physician.............. 56
The great Physician now is near 56
The Holy Spirit.................... 43
The Home over There 90
The Light of the World is Jesus. 42
The Lord's my shepherd, I'll not...... 101
The Lord will Provide 7
The New Song........................ 45
The Ninety and Nine 8
The Precious Name.................. 69
The Prodigal Child................. 39
There is a Fountain................. 89
There is a fountain filled with blood... 89
There is a gate that stands ajar....... 17
There is a land of pure delight........ 67
There is Life for a Look 78
There were ninety and nine that...... 8
The Spirit, oh, sinner,................ 43
The whole world was lost in the...... 42
The wondrous Gift.................. 50
This loving Saviour stands patiently .. 11
Till He Come........................ 68
Till He come, oh, let the words........ 68
'Tis the promise of God, full 4
To Day.................................. 55

PAGE

To-day the Saviour calls............... 55
To the hall of the feast came the...... 64

V.

Varina. C. M. D...................... 67

W.

Wandering afar from the dwellings... 14
We're Going Home To-morrow!... 24
We're going home, no more to roam... 24
Weary gleaner whence comest thou?.. 34
We praise Thee, O God................ 27
We shall meet beyond the river....... 9
We shall Meet By and By........ 9
What a Friend we have in Jesus. 30
What hast Thou Done for Me?... 23
What, "lay my sins on Jesus?"....... 54
What means this eager, anxious...... 10
What shall the Harvest be?..... 76
What various hindrances we meet 100
When He cometh, when He cometh... 95
When Jesus Comes................ 53
When the Comforter Came........ 98
Where are the Nine?.............. 14
Where hast Thou Gleaned?........ 34
White as Snow. 54
"Whosoever heareth," shout, shout... 12
Whosoever Will...................... 12
Wishing, Hoping, Knowing.......... 66
With harps and with viols, there...... 45
Wondrous Gift......................... 50
Wondrous Love....................... 31
Work, for the night is coming......... 107

Y.

Yes, there is Pardon for You..... 93
Yet there is Room 79
Yield not to Temptation........... 87

Page 220.